HEALTH ASSURANCE FOR ALL:
INSIDE AMERICAN HEALTH CARE

Health Assurance for All: Inside American Health Care

A CALL FOR CHANGE

By Michael Metzler

ISBN: 9798552284214

Library of Congress Number: 202092122

Cover Design: Maureen Metzler Norman

To Judy, whose love made me complete.

To Peg, whose love has made me complete again.

To Dave, Maureen, Joanna, and Kenton, along with their spouses and our grandchildren.

Thank you for all your joy and love.

The greatest joy of life is to love and be loved.
—R.D. Clyde

Table of Contents

Introduction

Over my career, I have been a frequent participant and observer in discussions about necessary changes to the American health care system. My experience on the subject spans a variety of roles. In my earlier career, I served as director of labor relations at a large retail corporation where I negotiated many collective bargaining agreements and served as a trustee on several union and management health plan boards. Subsequently, I transitioned to a human resources position at a hospital, became interested in operations, and moved up the ladder to a hospital CEO position. Over time, I have had lingering concerns about the degree of understanding that the public and policymakers have regarding the American health care system. Our system is extraordinarily complex. It can be a dangerous situation when policy and legislation are based on incomplete and erroneous suppositions. This book is an attempt to simplify our current system as well as to provide proposals for change.

I was initially inclined to write this book around the time of the 2012 presidential election due to the debate over the continuation of the Affordable Care Act (aka "Obamacare"). I hoped to provide a resource for the debate in simple form. However, I abandoned the effort. I felt the discussion and literature surrounding the 2012 election, as well as the 2016 election, raised the level of understanding to an acceptable level. However, as I listened to the Democratic presidential candidates in the debates for the 2020 election, I realized we still have a way to go when it comes to reaching the level of understanding necessary to make the right decisions. The newly debated options include "Medicare for All," a public option, and expanding or replacing the Affordable Care Act.

My attempt here is not to define and explain every last element of the American health care system but to concentrate on the major parts and how they interrelate. This book is designed to broaden the understanding of American health care consumers, the public, and the politicians who will make critical decisions on change. So I offer this book in the spirit of providing a primer, or simplified understanding, of our complex health care system. It is not meant to be a compendium of all health care terms. There are excellent books and publications serving that purpose, and they may be a better resource for college-level courses. Other terms and concepts not covered here are usually variations or expansions on the basics.

After providing simple explanations of the way health care works in the United States, my primary focus is on building a better health care system for all. The most important goals are improving population wellness and outcomes in a safe provider environment while ensuring everyone has the ability to afford timely and high-quality care. This book will focus on health *assurance* and how it results from different models of health *insurance*. The complex elements of our current system breed inequality of health assurance based on demographics and economic status. Our debates should always start with goals and move to plan designs that achieve them. This is based on the wisdom of working backward from vision and goals. The goals for health care should be derived from a vision of health assurance for all.

I have tried to avoid a personal opinion on the best health care system design for America. My goal is to provide a clear understanding of the pluses and minuses of different models under discussion in the political arena. I compare our system with those in other countries. Unfortunately, we will never discover a design that is a perfect win. Every possible model will combine gains with sacrifices. However, a better understanding of how everything works, and what stands to be gained from different models, will help drive the right priorities and choices.

My opinions do come through on goals and priorities. There are inequities and barriers to health assurance in the American system. I do not believe we are ready for wholesale change, but continuous, positive movement should be the call for action. My overarching objective is for policymakers and the public to understand the ramifications of alternative designs. I hope readers will gain a fuller understanding of how health care works and become conversant on how goals can be achieved or compromised. There is nothing worse than implementing a design that produces unintended results. The complexity of health care heightens this risk. Armed with knowledge, the electorate can be a driving force in steering policymakers in the right direction. We cannot afford mistakes or fail to make progress on policies affecting not just some aspects of life but life itself.

CHAPTER 1

A Few Simple Terms and Concepts

U nderstanding health care begins with the right definition of "health care system." We often refer to the US health care system or the health care systems in other countries. In the strictest form, the definition is "the organization of people, institutions, and resources that deliver health care services to meet the health needs of target populations" (Wikipedia, "health system," October 4, 2020). There is often confusion about the roles of the many players within a health care system. What is a provider, an insurer, a third-party payer, a health plan, an employer health plan, a government plan, etc.? A basic understanding of terms is necessary before discussing their roles under different proposed designs of the American health care system.

Let's start with the term "provider," sometimes referred to as a "caregiver." A provider is any person, institution, or organization providing direct care to a patient. The most well-known providers are doctors, but the term includes a vast array of caregivers, including but not limited to nurses, therapists of all sorts, nurse practitioners, X-ray technicians, and phlebotomists. They are the people we encounter at hospitals, physician offices, and outpatient clinics. They use their hands and minds for critical tasks such as administering tests, making diagnoses, and performing surgery.

A health care facility, organization, or institution is where caregivers are found and do their work. They include hospitals, physician offices, clinics, labs, surgery centers, and a myriad of other places. Caregivers may be employees and even owners of health care facilities.

Health plans, or health care insurance plans, are primarily the vehicle for financing the delivery of health care services. Throughout the book, I use the full term "health care insurance plans" to avoid confusion. Plans are not providers. They are financial entities offering services as third-party payers. The patient is the first party, the provider is the second party, and payers, or insurers, are the third party. Third-party payers collect insurance premiums and use the proceeds to pay, on behalf of their enrollees, the bills covered (insured) by the plan. Individuals and employers pay those premiums to the health plans. When individuals are in a government plan, such as Medicare, the government pays the premiums, and often those in the plan also pay a portion. Put very simply, the third parties pay the bills using revenue they receive from the premiums paid by individuals in the plan or paid on their behalf by their employer or the government. Bills submitted to the plans by providers for payment are often referred to as "claims." After a plan enrollee receives services as a patient, a provider issues a bill. The bill is sent to the plan as a claim for payment. The plan will then pay the portion it insures under its coverage provisions. The patient is responsible for any remaining balance.

There are various terms for people who participate in a plan. They are sometimes referred to as enrollees or members. A specific employee who enrolls in an employer-provided health care insurance plan for his or her family is sometimes said to be the subscriber. Participants in government plans are sometimes called beneficiaries or recipients. In the spirit of simplicity, I will use enrollee or participant to apply to all.

It is important to distinguish the general differences among plans in terms of who administers the plan and who generally participates or enrolls. To begin, there is a distinction between public and private plans.

Private health care insurance plans are called commercial plans. They are offered and administered by for-profit companies (insurance companies such as United, Cigna, and Prudential) and nonprofit organizations (such as Blue Cross Blue Shield and Kaiser Permanente). Both types offer an array of plans to be bought by individuals and by employers for their employees. Plans are designed with different coverages for different provider services. For example, one plan could cover all provider service costs while the patient is hospitalized. The price or premium of such a plan would be higher than one where the patient pays a portion of the costs. Alternatively, a plan could cover 80 percent of costs for hospitalization, with the patient paying the remaining 20 percent out-of-pocket. This patient portion is known as a co-payment. Lower premium plans are available, covering less than 100 percent of the cost of provider services. A plan may include many types of co-payments for visits to doctors or the emergency room such as requiring its enrollees to pay $100 for a visit to the emergency room or $20 for a visit to a doctor.

Patients may owe another type of out-of-pocket payment. It is called a deductible and is defined as the amount patients must pay providers within a given year before the third-party plan pays anything. For example, a plan may pay 100 percent of all provider service bills in a year, but not until the patient pays the first $500 incurred from the beginning of that year.

Health plan coverage for health care provider services is a matter of choice. In a competitive private market, one can choose from a variety of different plans offered by various third-party payers. Choice takes place in many forms. First, within each health plan (offered by an insurance company or nonprofit organization), there are options for levels of coverage. In a so-called Cadillac plan, everything is paid by the plan. Other options are typically available with the opportunity for the patient to accept lower levels of coverage by their plan, which means they take the risk of paying more or less out of pocket in the form of deductibles and co-payments. They pay less in premiums for accepting this risk.

Individuals who purchase health plans for themselves may have a myriad of coverage choices across many companies and nonprofit organizations. In the United States, more than half of working Americans participate in a health plan through their employers. The employer decides what plan choices will be available to its employees. The employer also decides what portion, or percentage, of the premium will be borne by the employees. The employee portion is called coinsurance and is usually collected by the employer as a payroll deduction. An employer can offer plans from various companies or organizations, and a single company could offer a variety of plans with different costs to employees, depending on how much cost is covered for provider services. I might choose a plan with high co-payments and deductibles to incur a lower coinsurance payroll deduction.

As opposed to private plans, our government offers plans for certain eligible population segments. The government is the third-party payer for provider services in the private sector. There are two major plans, namely Medicare and Medicaid.

Under Medicare, the federal government pays for provider services for people who are age sixty-five and over, as well as those under age sixty-five who are fully disabled under certain criteria. Under what is called "Part A," Medicare does not pay for 100 percent of costs when a patient is hospitalized (inpatient costs) but requires recipients of Medicare coverage to pay a portion. For Medicare to pay costs for services outside a hospital (referred to as outpatient costs or "Part B" of Medicare coverage), Medicare recipients must pay a monthly premium.

Medicaid is a government plan wherein costs are shared between the federal and state governments. It pays the cost of provider services for those who are unemployed or receive no health plan through their employers. Eligibility is based on household income.

The simple mechanisms of insurance apply to most health plans, which are run by private companies, nonprofit organizations, or the government. Whether applicable to car repairs or "people repairs," the elements of insurance are the same. The premium charged is the revenue received to cover claims or the cost of repairs, administrative costs, and a profit, in the case of a for-profit insurance company.

Nonprofit health plan organizations do not have stockholders who expect to receive a portion of the profits. However, they do find it necessary to at least break even, and they budget for a surplus of revenue over costs. The government seeks to keep costs as low as possible, so it does not have to seek more revenue than necessary from taxpayers.

There are a few major ways to minimize health plan premiums and costs, which will be discussed in detail in subsequent chapters. An overarching goal for all private and public health care insurance plans is to structure the plan so participants receive high-quality health care services at the lowest possible cost.

Understanding issues of ethics and equity is critical for those segments of our population excluded from health care insurance. A key term to understand here is "preexisting conditions." This refers to an illness people may have when they are being considered for participation in a health plan. Until the Affordable Care Act was passed in 2010, states could allow health plans run by insurance companies to exclude individuals with preexisting conditions from health plan coverage or charge them a higher premium. Another important term found in the debate over the government's role in offering health plans is "universal coverage." It would apply if 100 percent of Americans were covered by a health plan.

There are many other terms and concepts besides those defined here, but the foregoing are the most important ones. Others will be defined along the way.

CHAPTER 2

Distinctive Features of the US Health Care System

Compared to most of the world, the American system of providing insured access to health services is employer-based. During World War II, the government imposed price and wage controls. Unable to raise wages, employers started offering paid health care insurance plans as a benefit to their employees. This has continued until today and is referred to by some as an accident of history. At first, the cost of a health care insurance plan was fully covered by employers themselves. Over the decades, this changed, as the cost of health care services accelerated with new discoveries, new technologies, and new drugs. Employers found that the cost of this benefit became too large, and they began requiring employees to pay a portion of the premium, or "coinsurance."

Beginning in the 1980s, other forms of employee cost sharing evolved. Employers felt that unnecessary use of health care services could be mitigated if employees were required to pay a portion of the cost of a health care service, such as a visit to the doctor or emergency room. This became known as a co-payment. Enrollees would have "skin in the game" and maybe think twice before using a service unnecessarily. A variation on the same principle was charging a deductible, in which case an employee may have been required to pay, for example, the first $500 of all services in a year. Because of the rate at which they have increased in recent years, the financial impact of co-payments and deductibles on individuals and families has taken center stage in the discussion about health care insurance costs.

According to the Kaiser Family Foundation *2019 Employer Health Benefits Survey* (Kaiser Family Foundation, September 25, 2019), the annual premium cost of employer-sponsored health care insurance plans averaged $7,188 for single coverage and $20,576 for family coverage. Employees paid a coinsurance average of $1,242, or 17 percent of the premium, for single coverage and $6,015, or 29 percent of the premium, for family coverage. Among all employer-offered plans, 82 percent had annual deductibles. The annual deductible for single plans averaged $1,655. For almost all plans, employee cost also included co-payments for doctor visits, other services, and prescription drugs.

Typically, employee contributions toward premiums are not scaled by income, and everyone in the workplace pays the same fixed amount. So employees with lower salaries will pay higher percentages of their incomes. This can be a very significant difference. The average employee family plan's contribution of $7,188 represents 7.2 percent of a $100,000 salary and 18 percent of an hourly worker's annual wages of $40,000. In the United States, only about a quarter of employers with health care insurance benefits have salary-based contributions. Over the last decade, wages have risen less than health care insurance premiums, so fixed contributions have become a growing portion of employee wages.

Our health care system is primarily one of private providers and many private health plans. Doctors and other caregivers are typically employed by private organizations or self-employed. Health care institutions, such as hospitals and clinics, are privately owned. Private insurance companies, such as Prudential, United Healthcare, and Cigna, or nonprofit organizations, such as Blue Cross Blue Shield, Tufts, and Kaiser Permanente, offer health plans. As defined in Chapter 1, health plans are the payers. They pay the bills incurred by plan members or enrollees. We have a large number of health plans in our country, which makes us a multipayer health care system.

On both the provider and payer sides, although the US system is mostly private, there are publicly owned and operated facilities, such as veterans' and military hospitals and clinics. On the health plan side, there are government-run plans, or payers - namely, Medicare and Medicaid.

Medicare came into existence in 1965, during the Johnson administration, as a health care insurance plan for people age sixty-five and older, as well as those under sixty-five who are fully disabled. There was no coverage for prescription drugs until 2003, during the Bush administration. Medicaid began in 1965, serving low-income Americans without any health plan coverage. In 2010, the Affordable Care Act expanded Medicaid coverage for incomes up to 138 percent of the federal poverty level. It also instituted a tax subsidy towards private health care insurance premiums on a sliding scale for incomes up to 400 percent of the poverty level.

The American system is a hybrid system, but it is largely privately owned and privately insured. This is in contrast to other countries. In some countries, such as England, Sweden, and New Zealand, the health care system is entirely public. The government

9

owns and operates all health care facilities and employs all the providers working therein. This model is referred to as "socialized medicine."

In addition, everyone in a country with socialized medicine is enrolled in the same health care insurance plan. It is the government plan, and it is the only payer, or "single payer." The government pays for health care insurance coverage using tax revenue. Income tax rates are much higher in these countries to cover this expense, so there is an indirect cost to citizens. The plus side is that everyone in the country has health care insurance through the government plan. In other words, there is universal coverage.

There are international variations on the system just described. Canada has universal coverage through a single-payer government plan. However, Canadian health care providers are in the private sector. Doctors are not government workers, and hospitals are privately owned. All citizens are covered in the government plan, which is funded by tax revenue, resulting in a higher income tax rate than in the United States. So Canada has a single-payer system and universal coverage, but not socialized medicine.

The current debate over the right health care system in the United States divides into distinct camps. Presently, there is no advocacy for socialized medicine, where the government owns or employs health care providers and institutions. However, there is advocacy for a single-payer system and universal coverage. The specifics of this debate are covered in a later chapter.

CHAPTER 3

Private Health Care Insurance Plan Market

As an economist, I like to talk about economic principles in the framework of markets. A market is where buyers (or consumers) and sellers come together to make exchanges. In today's world, consumers exchange some form of money (cash, credit cards, etc.) for products or services. Markets are not necessarily physical places like supermarkets. Transactions now often take place in the virtual marketplace of the internet. Sometimes we do not transact directly, but rather through a third party. Amazon is a third party, as it offers a product at a specific price, accepts our money, and then gives that money to a seller, who either sends the product to us directly, or has the product sent to us from an Amazon warehouse (fulfillment center). Amazon does not make the product but serves as a third party between the two other parties, namely the seller and the consumer.

In our health care system, a consumer can buy an insurance plan to cover health services like diagnostic tests, hospital stays, and doctor visits. Rather than pay for the health care services directly, the plan pays the service providers: doctors, hospitals, labs, etc. The health care insurance plan is the third party between the consumer (or patient) and the provider. Health care insurance plans, despite their advertising that gives an impression to the contrary, do not serve as providers of health services. They serve a third-party (middle person) role between the purchaser and provider, just like Amazon.

Premiums may be paid to health care insurance plans solely by individuals or by employers on their behalf. Very typically, in our employer-based health care system, employers pay a significant amount of the premium, with the remainder paid by employees through payroll deductions. The employee portion is referred to as coinsurance. The cost-sharing percentage is decided by the employer or agreed on in negotiations between an employer and a union.

Often not fully understood is how the price of the health care insurance plan, or the premium, is calculated. Understanding this begins with the concept of insurance. Like car insurance, we want health care insurance to cover us in the case of unexpected events. When you pool a large group of people in a health care or car insurance plan, the sum of all individual premiums is expected to cover all insured events. Most people will have no or few events, so their cost to a plan would be less than their individual annual premiums.

The Sellers
In the private sector, there are sellers of health care insurance plans that can be either for-profit companies or not-for-profit organizations. The for-profit companies have a mission of making money for their owners, who may be stockholders. A board of directors manages them. Not-for-profit organizations have boards but not owners. Their mission is to serve their members (participants in

their plan) rather than make a profit. Examples of for-profits are United Healthcare, Prudential, and Aetna. Blue Cross Blue Shield, Harvard Pilgrim, and Kaiser Permanente are examples of not-for-profit organizations.

As companies and organizations operate in the market and look for what they will offer at a given price, they focus on cost and profit. Not-for-profit organizations do not look for a profit, but they want to keep their costs lower than the premiums they collect. Other ways of expressing this is that these organizations want to have a positive bottom line or a surplus. This provides a reserve for future years when circumstances might produce a loss. For-profit companies want to produce a surplus, or profit, for the same reason. They also want to distribute dividends and produce stock appreciation for their stockholders.

For both for-profit and not-for-profit insurance companies and organizations, the cost variables are the same. The greatest element is the total cost of all payments to health care providers for services rendered to plan participants in a year. This number is typically in the 80 to 90 percent range. The next greatest element, typically between 10 and 20 percent, is the cost of administering the system of payments to providers. A plan is a third party. Premium payments come in from buyers or participants, and payments to providers go out. Providers are sellers, in that they offer their services at an agreed-upon price. As the third party, the plan pays the bills, which are referred to as "claims." Providers submit claims to the plan, rather than to their patients.

As mentioned, the biggest percentage of health care plan costs is the cost of claims for provider services. This is a product of the quantity of services used by participants and the prices paid to providers. The amount a health care insurance plan pays to providers is determined by the negotiated contract between a plan and providers. Plans are often distinguished by the array or panel of providers whose services are insured for payment when participants use them. Not all providers in a geographic area may participate in every plan. They may choose not to participate because they are unable to negotiate prices they find acceptable.

As is true for all negotiations, each party's results depend on its bargaining power. If a health care insurance plan is one of only a few plans and has a large market share (near monopoly), it will be in a better position to negotiate lower prices. A hospital or physician group stands to lose a large percentage of patients if it cannot agree on prices and fails to be included among other providers in one of only a few available plans in its area.

As a general principle when it comes to negotiating prices, bigger is better whether you are a health care plan or a provider. The trend over the years, in many regions, has been consolidation on both the provider and health plan sides. Just as health care insurance plans have merged into a few large entities, there have been provider mergers and the creation of health care systems. These are provider health care systems, as opposed to a national health care system as defined in Chapter 1. These provider systems are generally comprised of a number of hospitals, a large physician group, and other entities such as clinics and imaging centers. These have evolved to develop large market shares for acquiring bargaining power in negotiations with large health care insurance plans. Solo or small group physician practices have evaporated, as physicians increasingly belong to large groups within provider health care systems that can negotiate on their behalf.

Bargaining power may produce different prices for the same provider services in the same region. Health care insurance plans seek to have in their networks large, prestigious hospitals with renowned physicians, as an attraction for enrollees. The same applies in the case of a system with a large number of hospitals located in many communities. A health care insurance plan does not want to lose such systems. So large health care systems will have more bargaining power to negotiate higher prices. This impacts not just the large, prestigious hospitals, but smaller hospitals and affiliated physicians in the same system located in different communities. Higher payments by insurers allow for greater financial resources among hospitals in large systems compared to hospitals in smaller systems. More financial resources will give a community an edge when it comes to providing better technology and staffing for their patients. Variations in access to quality health care from community to community are an example of inequality stemming from the model of private health care insurance plans within the American health care system.

Prices are not the same everywhere, which has consequences for the level of health care available depending on where one lives. This is in contrast to provider pricing in government plans (Medicare and Medicaid), which is legislated and largely the same within defined regions. There is some variation allowed for differences in cost-of-living and for hospitals with a disproportionate share of poorer patients.

The Buyers

The demand side of the health care insurance market is comprised of the buyers. These are mostly the employers who offer plans for their employees. Employees are the ultimate buyers, as they can choose their plans, but they have no role in determining the plan prices, called premiums.

Individuals who do not have access to health care insurance plans through an employer may purchase coverage directly from a plan. This is referred to as the "individual market." These individuals may be unemployed, self-employed, or simply working for a company not offering health care insurance. The individual market represents about 5 percent of the total US private and government health care insurance plan market.

The individual market is a complex study and has changed over time. The Affordable Care Act has lowered premiums in the individual market by offering coverage in large state exchanges (online marketplaces within a state), where claims are averaged across a large number of enrollees. There is more about this in Chapter 5.

Potential buyers of health care insurance (employers and individuals) choose to purchase plans, among the many available in the market, based on a three main factors:

1. Obviously, the cost or premium to participate in a given plan.

2. The providers offering services that will be insured within a given plan. Not all providers in a given geography may have a contract with a plan. Buyers want to be satisfied with the panel and the quality of the doctors and hospitals in the plan's directory. A plan will have contracts with the hospitals and doctors that agree to charge negotiated prices.

3. The quality of a plan's claim-paying process and customer service. For example, participants do not want to be billed by a hospital for services their plan incorrectly refused to accept They also want friendly and knowledgeable people

available to answer their inquiries such as questions about covered services, and about difficulties they have had when accessing provider services.

Health care insurance plans compete for buyers, based on these factors. Their marketing materials promote a fair premium for access to a large directory of quality providers and excellent customer service.

In summary, the market for health care insurance plans is quite similar to markets for other services and goods. Prices are set by the forces of supply and demand, with varying competitive characteristics depending on the number of competing plans and the size of provider organizations. The question for thought, here, is this: to what degree can market forces and characteristics, through independent operations and without government control, meet goals set for the American health care system?

CHAPTER 4

Provider Pricing Models and Cost

A health care insurance plan aims to keep provider service prices low, in order to set the lowest possible premium for its enrollees. In making a case for higher prices, a hospital, for example, might argue that it needs higher pricing to cover labor and supply inflation, the cost of new technologies, and higher salaries required to recruit and retain physicians and nurses. Provider pricing is the driver of premium pricing. Difficult negotiations over pricing are common, as plans argue with providers about the need to better manage their costs.

In Chapter 3, I used the term "prices" in the way it is generally understood. The meaning of "price" in health care is more complex than what generally applies to other services and goods. Fee-for-service pricing has historically been the most common in health care. We are all familiar with this type of pricing in our everyday lives. It's the price on a label in a department store, the price coming up on the supermarket's monitor screen per a scan code, or the dollar price in an Amazon cart at checkout. That form of pricing existed in health care in the decades before the early '80s. By that time, it was becoming clear that the fee-for-service model was accelerating the cost of health care in the American system. Providers could easily increase their incomes and revenues simply by ordering more tests, scheduling more visits, and prolonging hospital stays. They had a built-in incentive to do more.

In response, Medicare introduced a new pricing model to help stem the rising cost of health care services. The model is called the DRG (diagnostic-related group) system. The DRG system abandons the fee-for-service approach and pays a single amount to a hospital for all services received by a patient with a specific diagnosis. In this context, the DRG system has become more aptly called a "payment system."

The DRG system is complex in its administration, although it is easy to describe in general terms. Let's say I have a heart attack, and I am admitted to the hospital, where I have open-heart surgery of a particular type. I stay in the hospital for seven days, during which time I have a number of tests, medications, hours of nursing care, and meals. No matter the specific cost of each of these services or the number of days I am an inpatient, the hospital receives a fixed-dollar amount set by Medicare for the DRG of my type of heart attack. Medicare sets the amount for what is determined to be the expected cost of efficient and quality care. The goal is to incentivize hospitals to design the care within the bounds of that payment. Since the system originated, Medicare has expanded it to include fixed payments to hospitals and doctors for diagnoses treated in clinics and other outpatient settings.

Private health plans have adopted a similar approach and experimented with other forms of payment called "capitation." Imagine a health plan with 25,000 members of different ages and health status profiles, all receiving a variety of services through a hospital and its affiliated physician group within a given year. In their negotiations with a health plan, the hospital and physicians would propose a monthly payment per member, which they expect to receive for providing services to those 25,000 members. Their proposal would be based on actual services provided in the past, as well as expected illnesses predicted from demographic characteristics, such as age. The plan would agree to pay a negotiated monthly amount for each of the 25,000 individuals, or a per-capita amount. The hospital and physician group would be incentivized to manage its costs carefully since it will receive no more than the capitated amount and can keep whatever is not spent.

The DRG and capitated payment systems are quite different from paying a fee for each service. A major concern is the potential for unacceptable quality. Providers are able to profit from reducing their costs and retaining the balance of payments for themselves. This could result in unacceptable quality for patients. The common example is discharging patients from the hospital before they are ready to go home. For this reason, there is now extensive quality monitoring of care and outcomes by health plans, together with the providers. Today's payment systems now include incentives and penalties based on quality measures, so physicians can work with hospitals to be both efficient and high in quality while maximizing their income.

The current and growing payment model is essentially capitation, but with more controls to ensure quality and wellness. Health care insurance plans agree to pay a fixed amount to an accountable care organization (ACO) for each patient they serve. ACOs are made up of hospitals, physician groups, and other providers. They are now easier to organize because of the evolution and growth of large health care systems. Payments are based on patients' health and demographic characteristics, principally age. There are financial rewards for keeping costs low, and penalties for high cost and unacceptable quality. Older capitation models had weak systems of rewards and penalties. In newer models, incentives are based on reducing costs by keeping patients well.

The payment models described so far are designed to channel the behaviors of providers away from unnecessary and expensive care. Under the fee-for-service payment system, providers gain financially by doing more as patients get sicker. Under the ACO and DRG models, providers can retain more of their payments by focusing on prevention and wellness.

Cost control can also be achieved by modifying patient behavior through health care insurance plan design. There are two plan designs for cost efficiency. These are distinguished from the foregoing payment models, which focus on providers' behaviors. The first is called managed care, with rules to steer patients away from accessing unnecessary and expensive care. The second offers rewards and penalties for participation in wellness programs.

Managed care plans will only cover certain services if patients obtain approvals before accessing care. The goals are to prevent payment for unnecessary services and require patients to seek the least-cost necessary services. Rather than permit me to go directly to the hospital or clinic for X-rays and other testing, a managed care health care plan may require me to get an approval from my primary physician, who may first need to examine me. Rather than deciding on my own to go to a physician specialist, I will rely on my primary physician to determine whether a visit to a specialist is necessary.

With regard to wellness programs, my health care plan or my employer may offer financial incentives or penalties that encourage me to practice a healthy lifestyle. My coinsurance amount in my employer plan may be reduced or increased based on factors like weight loss or gain and whether I had an annual physical. My plan may reimburse me for health club dues or the cost of attending a smoking cessation program. The goal is to reduce health care insurance premiums by incentivizing employees to practice lifelong wellness. Of course, this works only if employees are retained over many years. This is not the trend in our modern economy, as individuals more often work for several employers over their careers. Cost savings are more achievable in a single-payer system, where all citizens remain in the same plan throughout their lifetimes.

The challenge over the decades has been to redesign our health care system to make it less costly, without compromising quality and outcomes. In a later chapter, I compare the costs of our system with those in other developed countries. The unfortunate fact is that we spend a much larger portion of our resources on health care and do not achieve comparable outcomes. We have a lot to learn and gain from others.

CHAPTER 5

Government Health Care Insurance Plans and the Affordable Care Act

In government health care insurance plans, the cost of a plan for the government is determined the same way as it is for private plans, but with three major differences. As with private plans, the major portion of cost is what is paid out to providers for services. That cost is based on the price of provider services. In private plans, pricing is a result of negotiations with providers. In government plans, the pricing is dictated through legislation. The second difference is that the government does not seek to make profit. A third difference is that, depending on the efficiency of government operations, there can be lower administrative costs, as these are averaged over millions of participants (referred to as "economies of scale"). In the case of Medicare, administrative costs are less than 5 percent of overall costs, whereas in private plans, the administrative costs are in the area of 15 percent.

The principal government plans are Medicare and Medicaid. There are other plans available to particular population cohorts, such as the veterans' health insurance programs and the Children's Health Insurance Program (CHIP). In the spirit of simplification, I will focus only on Medicare and Medicaid representing about 91 percent of all participants in government plans. The distinctive elements of these two apply to all government plans, namely:

1. The amount paid to providers for services is dictated by the government (state or federal).

2. Eligibility for participation and coinsurance for enrollees is a function of age and income.

Medicare

Let's begin with Medicare. All citizens age sixty-five and older are eligible. In addition, those under sixty-five who meet certain criteria for total disability are also eligible, at no cost to them. Moving forward, I will refer only to the nondisabled cohort, age sixty-five and over. This cohort represents approximately 87 percent of the Medicare budget.

Each Medicare enrollee is required to pay a portion of the cost of Medicare as a monthly premium. Contrary to some public belief, Medicare is not free. The coverage for hospital inpatient services, called Part A, is free but does not cover all services at 100 percent. There are annual deductibles as well as co-payments. The portion of Medicare covering outpatient services, called Part B, requires each participant to pay a monthly premium, which varies by income. Part A and Part B together cover about 80 percent of health care expenses. For 2021, an individual with modified adjusted gross income (MAGI)—adjusted gross income from tax return plus tax-exempt interest—under $88,000 is required to pay $148.50 per month. There is a sliding income scale that tops off at a premium of $504.90 for individuals with MAGI exceeding $500,000. In the intermediate range, individuals with adjusted MAGI between $138,000 and $165,000 pay $386.10 per month. Even after paying the Part B premium, there are still out-of-pocket co-payments for various types of outpatient services. Prescription drugs are covered under Part D, in which enrollees are required to choose a plan from a private health care insurance company and pay a portion of the premium, with Medicare paying the remainder to the company.

There are private health care insurance plans to offset partially, or in full, the deductible and co-payments required by Parts A and B. These may provide benefits not available through Medicare. They are available for enrollment when a patient first signs up for Medicare, or during the annual open enrollment period from October 15 through December 7. Two options are available:

1. **Supplemental, or Medigap, plans.** Each insurance plan generally offers plan choices that vary by the amounts of deductibles and co-payments. The monthly premium varies from limited coverage for about $70 to full coverage of all deductibles and co-payments at $270 a month, or so. This is in addition to paying for Part B. Since these plans do not cover prescription drugs, it is necessary to separately purchase a Part D prescription drug plan.

2. **Medicare Advantage plans.** In 2003, legislation was passed to allow private health care insurance plans to provide comprehensive coverage for those aged sixty-five and over. So rather than choosing traditional Medicare with Part B, plus a supplemental plan and a Part D plan for prescriptions, an

individual may sign up with a private insurer for a comprehensive plan covering inpatient and outpatient services, as well as prescription drugs. Participants must still pay the Part B premium to Medicare. These plans cover some or all of the co-payments or deductibles in Medicare Parts A and B, depending on the premiums for different levels of coverage. As an enticement, a plan may include some benefits not covered by basic Medicare, such as payments toward eyeglasses, hearing aids, dental services, and drugs. These plans receive a legislated amount from Medicare for each individual and charge a monthly premium to participants. For 2021, the average monthly premium in the country is projected to be $21.00. This premium is significantly less than what an individual would pay for a supplemental (Medigap) plan. About one-third of Medicare enrollees participate in an Advantage plan.

It is important to understand why traditional Medicare (Parts A and B) plus a supplemental plan, together, typically cost more than paying for Part B plus a Medicare Advantage plan. It is all about choice of provider services and preapprovals. Under traditional Medicare and a supplemental plan, a recipient may seek services from any doctor, hospital, or outpatient facility, if such providers have a contract to provide services to Medicare patients. Since elderly patients use a significant portion of health care services in the United States, nearly all providers accept Medicare. Traditional Medicare enrollees may access services without any preapprovals.

Advantage plans negotiate their own pricing with providers, and typically do so within a limited network. Nearly all such plans are structured like a health maintenance organization (HMO) or preferred provider organization (PPO), with a limited network of providers and preapproval for services. In fact, providers in Medicare Advantage plan networks periodically renegotiate their contracts with insurers and may drop out of the network if they find payment rates to be unacceptable. So my favorite local hospital could become unavailable to me down the road, even if it is now in the network. This could also happen with providers in a supplemental plan, but it is historically less likely, and I could still go to almost any hospital or doctor under the Part A and Part B coverages with no requirement to receive a preapproval.

Research shows that participants in Medicare Advantage plans tend to be healthier than those choosing basic Medicare plus a supplemental plan. Advantage plans are therefore less costly, because they pay out less per participant for health care services, (i.e., claims per capita). What Medicare pays these plans per participant may be less than what is paid out for services to their members who are healthier than the average Medicare recipient. This correlates with how people make choices. Healthier individuals are apt to take more risk in limiting their provider choices with preapprovals by selecting an Advantage plan.

Until 2003, Medicare did not provide coverage for prescription drugs. At that time, prescription drugs became covered under a new Part D. Traditional Medicare enrollees are now required to purchase a Part D plan. Part D coverage is exclusively provided by the private insurance sector. A plan charges a monthly amount to generate enough revenue to cover drug purchases, plus administrative costs and profits. The federal government makes payments to the plans for each covered individual for about 75 percent of this amount, and the balance is charged monthly as a premium to each individual.

A variety of Part D plans are offered at differing premiums, depending on the annual deductible, co-payments, and the drugs covered. Each plan refers to its "formulary" of drugs covered by the plan. Expensive drugs may not be in the formulary, or they may require high co-payments. The open enrollment period is the same as for other Medicare plans. Medicare has a website where an individual is able to list their medications and get a calculation of the total annual cost of each plan—including the premium, annual deductible, and co-payments. There could be as many as twenty or so plans available in a more populated region, with monthly premiums varying from roughly $15 to $100.

As mentioned above, Medicare is not free. In fact, the cost to a participant may be as much as the monthly amount charged to a worker for an employer-sponsored health care insurance plan. The premium paid by traditional Medicare enrollees for Parts B and D increases on an income-based sliding scale and varies by an individual's or couple's gross income. Advantage plan enrollees pay more for Part B on the same scale. Here is how it approximately adds up in 2021 for individuals and per person in a couple:

2021 Medicare Monthly Premiums
Adjusted Gross Annual Income (in 000s) *

Individuals	<$88	$88-$111	$111-$138	$138-$165	$165-$500	>$500
Couples	<$176	$176-$222	$222-$276	$276-$330	$330-$750	>$750

Premiums for Traditional Medicare (see Medicare.gov) Plus a Medigap Plan (per person in a couple)

Part A	$0	$0	$0	$0	$0	$0
Part B	$148.50	$207.90	$297.00	$386.10	$475.20	$504.90
Part D**	$41.00	$53.30	$72.80	$92.20	$111.70	$118.10
Medigap***	$152.00	$152.00	$152.00	$152.00	$152.00	$152.00
TOTAL	**$341.50**	**$413.20**	**$521.80**	**$630.30**	**$738.90**	**$775.00**

Premiums for Part B Plus a Medcare Advantage Plan

Part B	$148.50	$207.90	$297.00	$386.10	$475.20	$504.90
Advantage Plan**** (Includes prescription drugs)	$21.00	$21.00	$21.00	$21.00	$21.00	$21.00
TOTAL	**$169.50**	**$228.90**	**$318.00**	**$407.10**	**$496.20**	**$525.90**

* This is simply a gross income from the federal tax return plus tax-exempt interest.

** Estimated 2021 average bid from "Medicare Part D: A First Look at Medicare Prescription Drug Plans in 2021," Kaiser Family Foundation, Juliette Cubanski and Anthony Damico, Oct 19, 2020.

*** 2019 national average from ehealthinsurance.com, eHealth Medicare, "How Much Does a Medicare Supplement Insurance Plan Cost?" 2020.

**** Average from "Medicare Advantage 2021 Spotlight: First Look," Kaiser Family Foundation, Jeannie Fuglesten Biniek, Meredith Freed, Anthony Damico and Tricia Newman, Oct 29, 2020.

Medicaid

Medicaid is the government health care insurance program for low-income individuals and families. Those residing in the thirty-eight states accepting Medicaid expansion (explained below) under the Affordable Care Act (ACA) are eligible, free of cost, if their income is 138 percent or less of the federal poverty level. The eligibility scale used varies by income and family size. In 2021, individuals are eligible if their income is below $17,609, and a family of four is eligible if their income is below $36,156.

A number of states refused to expand Medicaid coverage, in spite of the substantial federal subsidies available to them. As of November 2020, there were twelve states still not accepting Medicaid expansion. For the first four years of the ACA, these subsidies covered 100 percent of expansion costs. However, beginning in the fifth year of the ACA, the federal government gradually reduced the subsidy to 90 percent, and it now stands at that level indefinitely.

It is important to understand that there is a separate system of insurance and providers for Medicaid recipients. This system is far more limited in provider choice than the system most Americans enjoy through their employers, with commonly known insurers such as Blue Cross Blue Shield, United Healthcare, and Aetna. There are stories, for example, that Medicaid recipients have to travel long distances to find a physician specialist, because the local specialists do not accept Medicaid patients.

The legislated Medicaid payment rates to hospitals, doctors, and other providers are typically below both Medicare and private insurance plans. Hospitals, for example, argue that Medicaid fails to cover the cost of caring for patients. Many doctors will not accept Medicaid patients. To alleviate this gap, government-subsidized community health centers principally serve Medicaid patients.

Primary care doctors are employed at these centers and accept below-market salaries. Separate health insurance plans have been established, with a panel of providers willing to accept Medicaid patients. Their payments from the Medicaid program are funneled through these plans.

One last point on Medicaid: a large portion of Medicaid expenditures cover nursing home residents who are unable to pay the full cost of residency and care. Most of one's assets must be used first, but once they are nearly depleted, Medicaid pays the difference between the patient's income and the full cost. The annual cost could be $100,000, and the resident may, for example, only have Social Security and a pension income totaling $50,000. The American system has been generous in accommodating this essential need at a vulnerable stage in one's life.

Affordable Care Act

The Affordable Care Act provided for the expansion of Medicaid eligibility to those with higher incomes, as well as a tax credit toward private insurance premiums for those not poor enough for Medicaid eligibility.

Its purpose is to decrease the number of uninsured Americans. At the outset of ACA, there were about 47 million uninsured Americans. As of 2018, the estimated number stood at 8.5 percent of the population, or 27.5 million ("Health Insurance Coverage in the United States: 2018 U.S. Census Bureau," Berchick, Edward R., Jessica Barnett and Rachel D. Upton, Nov 8, 2019).

The expansion provision lifted the eligibility for Medicaid to 138 percent of the federal poverty level, to include more low-income Americans. Until that time, the percentage income poverty level cap varied by state, but was typically far below 138 percent. In

2012, the US Supreme Court ruled that states could refuse the expansion. As mentioned above, as of November 2020 there were still twelve states not accepting the expansion. In many of these states, low-income adults without dependent children are ineligible for Medicaid.

The tax subsidy (or credit) provision of the ACA is more complicated. Those not eligible for Medicaid, who have an income of up to 400 percent of the poverty level, are eligible for a tax credit if they buy their health care insurance from a government "exchange," or state marketplace. An exchange can be accessed on a website, where individuals are able to purchase a health plan from an assortment of private insurance plans in their state. There are four tiers of plans at varying levels of premiums, deductibles, and co-payments. The bronze, silver, gold, and platinum tiers cover 60 percent, 70 percent, 80 percent, and 90 percent of medical costs, respectively. The second lowest silver plan in a given state, is considered to be the benchmark for affordability calculations of the tax credit amount.

What follows is an explanation of how the tax credit works. There is a government table showing different percentages of the poverty level by family size, up to 400 percent (See "Explaining Health Care Reform: Questions About Health Insurance Subsidies," Kaiser Family Foundation, Oct 30, 2020). A second table lists what percentage of income (affordability percentage) is expected to be spent for health care insurance at each percentage of the poverty level in the first table (ibid.). The next step in the calculation is to see what the annual premium is for the second lowest, or benchmark, silver plan in a given state of residence. An individual would then multiply the percentage of the poverty level for their income times the premium for the silver benchmark plan. The difference between that amount and the silver plan premium is the tax credit. Individuals may receive a monthly advance of the tax credit and then reconcile the amount of credit on their federal tax return, based on their final yearly income. An individual could pick a plan in the gold or platinum tier but would receive only the tax credit based on the silver benchmark plan, resulting in a higher premium to pay.

Here is an example: a Pennsylvania resident in Philadelphia County with an income of $25,520 is at 200 percent of the poverty level and is expected to afford 6.51 percent of income toward a health care plan. The premium for the benchmark silver plan is $7,200 per year. This number is from the Pennsylvania exchange (called "Pennie"). The benchmark premium goes up with age and the example here assumes the resident is male and age 49.

Applying the affordability percentage of 6.51 percent to an annual income of $25,520, he is expected to afford $1,664 for health care insurance. Subtracting this from the benchmark silver plan premium of $7,200, this individual is eligible for a tax credit of $5,536. He could purchase a plan on the exchange that is more expensive but would receive only $5,536 and would then pay a higher amount than the $1,664. Below are more examples from Pennsylvania, assuming either one or two adults (both age 49) reside in the household. The premium for two adults is twice the premium for one. Whether children add to premium cost depends on whether they are eligible for the CHIP program, administered by Medicaid. The expected contribution would cover the benchmark silver plan.

2021 Tax Subsidy by Income Level
Philadelphia County (Zip Code 19019)

150% of Poverty Level

Household Size	Income	Premium	Expected Contribution (4.14%)	Subsidy
1	$19,140	$7,200	$792	$6,408
2	$25,860	$14,400	$1,071	$13,329

200% of Poverty Level

Household Size	Income	Premium	Expected Contribution (6.52%)	Subsidy
1	$25,520	$7,200	$1,664	$5,536
2	$34,480	$14,400	$2,248	$12,152

300% of Poverty Level

Household Size	Income	Premium	Expected Contribution (9.83%)	Subsidy
1	$38,280	$7,200	$3,763	$3,437
2	$51,720	$14,400	$5,084	$9,316

400% of Poverty Level

Household Size	Income	Premium	Expected Contribution (9.83%)	Subsidy
1	$51,040	$7,200	$5,017	$2,183
2	$68,960	$14,400	$6,779	$7,621

NOTE: Calculations have been made according to the "Pennie Plan Comparison Tool" at enroll.pennie.com/hix/preeligibility#/results.

Working individuals who have health care insurance as a benefit are eligible for a tax credit only if they purchase a plan from the exchange, not from their employer. They are not eligible to purchase from the exchange if the employer charges employees a portion of its plan premium below the affordability amount from the chart, provided that the coverage in the employer's plan is at least equivalent to the silver plan.

An intended takeaway from this chapter is the complexity of the US health care system. Just imagine the senior population trying to determine what plan is best and affordable. Then think of employees trying to do the same, during their employer's open enrollment period. Finally, although the ACA is meant to move our country to universal coverage, consider the challenge of individual citizens attempting to figure out whether they are eligible for Medicaid or for a tax credit based on their income.

Proposed new structures for the US health care system will be explained in Chapter 10. Whether participating in an employer-provided health care insurance plan or a government plan, Americans are required to navigate through a maze of choices and rules that, at times, produce unintended consequences. It would seem that, short of considering major new structures, there should be a movement toward major simplification of our health care system.

CHAPTER 6

The High Cost of the American Health Care System: How We Compare with Other Countries

The numbers are staggering, by themselves and in comparison to other countries. Nearly 18 percent of US gross domestic product (GDP) is spent on health care. Not every American has health care insurance. This differs from countries like England, Canada, Germany, France, and many others, where every citizen has access to health care, because there is universal insurance coverage supported through the general tax system. In other words, the government has its own health care insurance plan (national insurance). Income taxes are significantly higher in these countries to pay for the government plan, but the percentage of GDP spent on health care services is typically in the 9–12 percent range. So everyone has coverage, but overall spending is substantially less than it is in the United States. Before making comparisons, it is important to again explain different types of health care systems in developed and higher-income countries, like ours.

As explained in Chapter 2, the meaning of socialized medicine is often misunderstood. This refers in the strict sense to countries where the government owns provider facilities, such as hospitals and clinics, and all caregivers, including doctors, are government employees. In addition, these countries have a national single-payer health care insurance plan, operated by the government. Examples are Great Britain, the Scandinavian countries, and New Zealand. The Canadian system is sometimes incorrectly identified as socialized medicine, but Canadian provider facilities and caregivers are, respectively, privately owned and privately employed. Health care insurance is through a single-payer system run by the Canadian government. The political position of "Medicare for All" is akin to the Canadian model of a single insurance payer with private providers and facilities.

An important distinction of countries with socialized medicine or a single-payer system is how health care insurance is funded. The answer is, typically, through higher taxes. In the United States, on the nongovernment side, with a multitude of private insurance plans, employers pay a significant portion of premiums, and employees pay a portion referred to as coinsurance. Under Medicare, our government covers a large portion of the cost, with enrollees paying a portion according to their income. Medicare is essentially the single-payer system for those aged sixty-five and older.

One can imagine different combinations of characteristics that make up a country's health care system of providers and insurers. Germany has a private system of providers, in combination with single-payer insurance. However, the system is financed through the requirement that all employers and employees each pay 8 percent of the government-set premium. The majority of employers in the United States offering health care insurance as a benefit set a flat percentage of the premium as an employee co-payment rate, regardless of income.

Countries with universal coverage spend much less of their GDP on health care, but fare better on outcomes and health characteristics than people in the United States. Here are a few relative outcome measures, compared to spending:

International Comparisons on Outcomes and Spending: 2016

	Life (Years) Expectancy	Infant Mortality (Per 1,000 Births)	% Overweight	Health Care Spending (% of GDP)	(Per Capita)
USA	78.8	5.8	70.1	17.8	$9,403
Canada	81.7	5.1	60.3	10.3	$4,641
UK	81.0	3.9	62.9	9.7	$3,377
Germany	80.7	3.3	60.0	11.3	$5,182
France	82.4	3.8	49.0	11.0	$3,681
Japan	83.9	2.1	23.8	10.9	$3,727

Source: *Journal of the American Medical Association* (JAMA), "Health Care Spending in the United States and Other High-Income Countries," Irene Papanicolas, Ph.D.; Liana R. Woskie, MSc; Ashish K. Jha, MD, MPH, May 13, 2018.

For some important measures, we seem to get less value for our relatively higher spending. Why the difference, relative to other countries with similar economic characteristics? A number of reasons were revealed in the above study data by the *Journal of the American Medical Association*. Our utilization patterns are generally not different, our number of primary care providers and physician specialists are about the same per capita, and we do not have fewer social services to mitigate illness. The other countries insure all citizens at a lower cost than the United States does, yet our uninsured population is around 10 percent. I will go through the major reasons for our higher costs.

High Cost of Prescription Drugs

In 2016, the cost of retail prescription drugs in the United States was $328 billion, or about 10 percent of health care spending. According to a popular health affairs blog, when you add drug costs at hospitals, the total rises to $480 billion, or about 15 percent of health care spending ("Spending on Prescription Drugs in the U.S.: Where Does all the Money Go? *Health Affairs*, July 31, 2018). Prescription drug pricing is determined by supply and demand in our free market system, without any government controls on price. However, our government grants a monopoly to companies for newly discovered drugs, for a fifteen-year period. These are referred to as brand-name drugs. After fifteen years, the monopoly ends, and other drug companies may produce competitive drugs, called generic drugs, with substantially the same composition. With one or more drugs then competing with each other, prices decline. In countries with a single-payer system, the government fixes the prices for prescription drugs. Of the eleven countries with the highest income, the United States spent $1,443 per capita, compared to a range of $466 to $939 per capita, in the other countries. Even when you include the United States, the mean for all eleven countries was $749.

The overwhelming factor behind these differences is drug pricing. The comparisons are astonishing. It is difficult to get accurate US prices for comparison, because of the complexity of the pharmaceutical market. List prices do not represent what everyone pays, because there are middlepeople or brokers, called pharmacy benefit managers, who negotiate significant discounts and rebates for employer health care plans. Even with discounted rates, our drug prices remain much higher than those in other countries. In particular, uninsured Americans get charged high list prices. In recent years, new companies have been formed to negotiate discounts for members of the public who use their coupons. One example is GoodRx. Unless you know enough to find a coupon, you will likely be charged list price by a pharmacy. Even insured individuals with high-deductible drug insurance plans, including those with Medicare Part D, may find it cheaper to use a discount coupon than have the cost charged 100 percent to the deductible in their plan. I can report a personal experience at a chain pharmacy, where I ended up paying $75 rather than the $275 list price.

Without going into extensive detail, here are some of the astounding findings on US drug prices:

- A 2018 report ("A Painful Pill to Swallow: U.S. vs. International Prescription Drug Prices," September 2019) from the US House Committee on Ways and Means staff made several findings comparing prices in eleven other countries (UK; Ontario, Canada; Japan; Australia; Portugal; France; Germany; Switzerland; Denmark; Sweden). US list prices of seventy-nine drugs were found to be almost four times higher than the mean for the eleven countries. Even after factoring in rebates, the average US rebates would have to be over 73 percent just to match list prices in the other countries. Our Medicare program could save $49 billion if we just matched the average prices in the eleven other countries. It hasn't happened, because it is illegal for our government to negotiate prices in the pharmaceutical market. Congress bends to drug industry lobbying and refuses to legalize the negotiation of drug prices.

- A 2017 news release from pharmacychecker.com ("70% of Popular Brand Name Drugs Sold in U.S. Pharmacies Are Imported; Cost Up to 87% Less in Canada," August 3, 2017) reported that 70 percent of top-selling brand-name drugs are produced outside the United States and sold for 87 percent less in Canada and 97 percent less in other countries. Although the practice is illegal (but not prosecuted), it is not surprising that millions of Americans purchase their medications from Canadian sources.

- Drugs sold in the United States are 56 percent less in other high-income countries, including 67 percent less in France and 51 percent less in Germany ("U.S. Drug Prices vs. The World," drugwatch.com, Jul 27, 2020).

The consequences of high prescription drug prices can be dire for Americans. Surveys continue to show that a significant percentage of Americans forgo needed drugs, cut pills in half, skip doses, give up food, and go into bankruptcy because of their inability to pay for drugs. This includes those with private insurance and Medicare Part D, where the drug is not covered or has an exorbitant co-pay or deductible. Oral chemotherapy drugs now have an average annual cost of $150,000. Here is one story:

Keith [Lyons] said his father would be alive if it weren't for the impossible expense of a $1,000-per-pill treatment. The 12-week treatment for hepatitis C, which Gilead Sciences Inc. sells in the U.S.

as Sovaldi, costs around $84,000. But Lyons' father, Nicolas, couldn't afford it and was uninsured. When he went to the hospital, he was given only Vicodin for pain control.

The father and son couldn't scrape together enough money to send Nicolas to India, where a generic version of Sovaldi costs less than $10 per pill, and where he had dreamed of staying for the 12-week treatment described as a possible "miracle cure."

"He could have been alive for another 20 years," said Keith. His father died last September. He was 63. "He wanted to live and he wanted to do more for humanity than he got to do" ("A Bitter Pill: The Human Toll of Unaffordable Medicines," Interfaith Center on Corporate Responsibility, 2020).

Administrative Costs

The United States has hundreds of health care insurance plans, compared to single-payer systems in other countries. Each plan has its own administrative structure for payment, management, overhead, marketing, etc. Providers incur significant expense to comply with the requirements and administrative payment processes for a myriad of health care plans. Caregivers lose valuable time with patients because they are busy performing the administrative tasks necessary to process and receive payment for services.

When comparing our health care system with other countries, administrative costs are divided into two categories. The first category is for the costs for private and government plans to process and manage the receipt and payment of claims. The second is the cost incurred by providers (principally hospitals, clinics, and physician practices) to process their claims for payment. In countries with single-payer systems, there is only one plan, with one set of rules, so you would expect administrative costs to be less for the government entity running the plan. This would also be the case for providers who submit claims according to a single set of rules and identical coverage for all patients. Single-payer plans also have the opportunity to enjoy significant economies of scale.

The data is quite revealing. The Center for American Progress studied comparisons from a variety of sources, on both categories of cost. The Centers for Medicare and Medicaid Services (CMS), a US government organization, estimated that 2019 billing and insurance related (BIR) costs incurred by private plans and government plans was $214 billion, and $282 billion was spent by hospitals, physician practices, and other providers for processing costs. Other studies resulted in larger estimates, but included expenses not captured by CMS. The one comparison that studies find to be in relatively close range, or within a close magnitude of variation, is the difference in BIR costs between Medicare and private health care insurance plans. Studies calculate Medicare BIR costs to be in a range of 2 to 5 percent, compared to around 17 percent for private plans. Medicare is a single-payer, government-run plan, able to achieve large economies of scale.

The Center for American Progress also reported on the international health system data of the Organization for Economic Cooperation and Development. The organization used its definition of administrative expenses for private and government health care plans incurred only by the plans themselves, and not by hospitals, physicians, and other providers. They found that in 2016, the United States spent 8.3 percent of total health care expenditures on administrative costs. The range for thirteen other high-income countries was from 6 percent in Norway to 5.7 percent in Germany. Countries with single-payer systems had costs among the lowest. (See "Excessive Administrative Costs Burden the U.S. Health Care

System," Center for American Progress, Emily Gee and Topher Spiro, April 8, 2019.

Wages and Prices

The Journal of the American Medical Association article quoted earlier in this chapter also reported on caregiver wages in eleven countries. Here, again, the United States is an outlier. Physician generalists in the United States averaged $218,173 in annual pay, compared to an average of $133,173 for all countries. The average for these physicians in Germany was $154,126, and in Canada, $146,286. Physician specialists earned an average of $316, 000 in the United States, and $182,657 on average, for all of the eleven countries. US registered nurses made an average of $74,160, compared to a mean of $51,795 for all eleven countries in the database.

The International Federation of Health Plans, in partnership with other organizations, published a *2017 Comparative Price Report* on the prices of medical services in nine countries. Prices were based on what is paid by private insurance plans, rather than "charges," which are the highest list prices of providers. For nearly all services, US prices were higher than the median of all prices in the database. Here is a sampling.

2017 International Price Comparisons (in US dollars)

Procedure	USA	UK	Australia	New Zealand	Switzerland
Angioplasty	32.2K	11.7K	14.7K	*	7.4K
Bypass Surgery	78.1K	24.4K	35.8K	*	32.0K
Knee Replacement	29.6K	12.7K	18.6K	17.6K	18.3K
Hip Replacement	32.5K	12.2K	20.9K	16.6K	15.6K
Normal Delivery	11.2K	9.0K	6.1K	*	5.1K
CT Scan Abdomen	1.1K	0.47K	*	0.58K	0.33K
MRI Scan	1.43K	0.45K	*	0.75K	0.31K
Cardiac Cath	7.09K	2.45K	*	*	1.55K
Appendectomy	13.02K	3.05K	*	6.71K	*

*No data available

It is not surprising that American employers, as part of their health care plans, have begun offering fully paid travel to other countries for costly procedures.

In summary, though one can argue about some flaws in the data, the order of magnitude gives one pause. We spend 40 percent to 100 percent more on just about everything. In spite of this, we are behind other developed countries on outcomes. There is a clear message about the need for change. Excess spending on health care could be used to improve the quality of life for many Americans, including providing health care insurance for the 10 percent who still have none.

CHAPTER 7

Choice

The title of this chapter seems to be the word most used by politicians in the debate over health care. On its face, choice is synonymous with democracy in the American lexicon. If there is not full understanding of the implications or context, there is immediate repulsion over any hint of losing choice. In health care, choice is clearly something we value and may be willing to pay more to preserve or expand.

Individual choice is sacred. We abhor someone else making choices for us. Politicians easily win on their health care positions by claiming an opponent's position will take away choice. It is the political dividing line between adopting Medicare for All as a single-payer system versus keeping the current system of many choices of health care insurance plans.

Many have a quick emotional reaction to potentially losing their choice of an array of health care insurance plans, despite the reality of who makes the decisions on individual participation in a health insurance plan. In our employer-based health insurance system, the employer decides what plan or plans to offer. Employees do not have employer-paid access to just any health insurance plan in the market. There is limited choice at the workplace, and not all the available options may be favorable in the eyes of an employee.

It has been my experience that when an employer announces its decision on health insurance plan offerings for the next year, employees immediately ask if their choices of hospitals and doctors are included in each plan. Their overriding concern about choice is whether they will have their choice of providers. Employees are at the mercy of their employer's choice of plans, which may or may not include their preferred providers.

Employers generally offer a variety of plans with different choices of providers. The greater a plan's network of providers, the greater the premium. I may wish to lower my cost for a plan by limiting my provider choices. There are other features to keep the premium lower, but one may be the offer of a limited number of providers who have agreed to a plan's lower payment rates for services.

Plan types characterized by more limited provider networks are:

- **HMOs (health maintenance organizations)**—These plans became popular in the '80s as the cost of health care began accelerating. Besides having a specific panel of providers (a network), these plans typically require approval before enrollees can access specialty services, such as visits to a physician specialist, and high-cost diagnostic procedures, such as MRIs. There is no coverage for services accessed by an enrollee outside the network.

- **PPOs (preferred provider organizations)**—These plans are similar to HMOs, offering a defined list of providers (a network). The plan pays the full cost of services, or near full cost. However, the plan will pay only a portion of the cost of services outside the network. The enrollee co-payment outside the network is typically as high as 25 percent. This translates to significant dollars in the case of expensive hospitalizations, surgeries, and treatments. Compared to an HMO, the out-of-network option is attractive, because it preserves choice, albeit an expensive one. It gives comfort in the event of a serious health issue, if patients feel a provider outside the network is more highly skilled and offers higher quality, compared to alternatives within the network.

Provider choice is also an issue for enrollees in government plans. Traditional Medicare, with Part A for inpatient services and Part B for outpatient services, offers nearly unlimited choice within a national network of providers that contract to accept Medicare patients. As described in Chapter 5, those eligible for Medicare may choose either a private supplemental plan (Medigap) to offset the deductibles and co-payments under traditional Medicare, or they may select a Medicare Advantage plan. There is a premium for supplemental plans, and the plans continue the unlimited provider choice under Parts A and B. The Advantage plans are less expensive. They cover what is insured under traditional Medicare, as well as some or all of the uncovered gaps, but must be used within a limited provider network, as in an HMO or PPO.

Medicaid, the government's second-largest health care insurance plan, is important to discuss, regarding choice. As explained in Chapter 5, providers are paid the lowest prices for treating Medicaid patients, when compared to Medicare and private plans. Medicaid enrollees are individuals and families with low income, and the government subsidizes the premium on a sliding scale based on income. Because of the low prices, many providers choose not to offer services to Medicaid patients. So lower-income Americans have the least provider choice, compared to all others. Community health centers are established with government financial support to principally serve this population segment. In these centers, dedicated caregivers receive submarket wages.

Americans have legitimate concerns about being limited by their employers to plans where they have experienced poor customer service. They may relate stories to others, and sometimes to government agencies (e.g., an attorney general's office), in the form of complaints. Enrollees are sometimes billed incorrectly for services covered by the plan. This may be the result of poor administrative plan practices, including long delays in payments to providers. Other complaints are about rigid plan rules that lead to denial of claims. This could be caused by an enrollee's failure to get a preapproval for a service, or the submission of incorrect or incomplete information on a claim, by either the patient or the provider.

So choice is a genuine big issue. Individuals who buy insurance on the open market and pay the full premium are able to exercise choice in the fullest sense. For the vast majority of our population, there are limitations on choice. The amount of provider choice depends on how much one is willing and able to pay. Being over age sixty-five, I may be able to afford only a Medicare Advantage plan with fewer choices of providers than I'd gain by selecting traditional Medicare plus a supplemental plan, which includes almost unlimited provider choice. A low-income, perhaps unemployed, Medicaid enrollee has the least choice of providers. If I get my health insurance through my employer, I am limited to the plans my employer offers. My employer may offer an array of plans with broad or limited provider networks. However, given the portion of the premium I am required to pay out of my paycheck (my coinsurance), I may be able to afford only the plan with the fewest provider choices, or I may not be able to afford any of the plans and choose to be uninsured.

There is clearly variation in our population, when it comes to the cost of coverage and access to providers based on age, income, employed versus unemployed, and place of employment. The question for further thought is whether the American health care system could be structured differently to give opportunity for every American to access the same quality and level of services they need to be as healthy as they can be. Answering this question is the challenge for the remaining chapters.

CHAPTER 8

The Goal of Health Assurance for All

The goals I will outline here are largely, but not unanimously, supported by the American public. There are clearly significant differences over how to achieve these goals, how we design our health care system to support them, and whether or how we pay for them. Before this discussion, it is important to pause and consider what we generally wish to achieve.

At the time of the passage of the Affordable Care Act in 2010, there were approximately 47 million Americans without any health care insurance. The main goal of the legislation was to reduce this number to almost zero. As of late 2018, this number has been reduced by about 19 million, leaving over 28 million Americans without health insurance. Uninsured Americans are entitled to receive treatment when they appear at a hospital emergency room for episodic care. However, they do not have a primary physician, preventive care through screenings, or regular care for chronic diseases. Detection of serious illness typically happens too late. Much analysis has been done to demonstrate that the cost of care in the

American health care system, as a whole, would be less if everyone had health care insurance coverage. This way, patients could have their health evaluated periodically, rather than waiting for serious episodes that lead to costly care.

It is argued by many that universal health care insurance coverage is a right, rather than a privilege. The Declaration of Independence gives us the right to life, liberty, and the pursuit of happiness. Being as healthy as possible certainly falls within the meaning of this language. As revealed in a recent poll of the Pew Institute, "Six-in-ten Americans say it is the federal government's responsibility to make sure all Americans have health care coverage..." (Pew Research Center, "Most continue to say ensuring health care coverage is government's responsibility," Jocelyn Kiley, October 3, 2018).

A second goal, generally supported, is that no one should be denied health care insurance if they have an illness. This is often referred to as being denied because of a preexisting condition. Until the passage of the Affordable Care Act, states allowed health care insurance plans to deny enrollment to individuals with an illness or charge them much higher premiums. Those arguing for the acceptability of this practice have said that the American capitalist system of free enterprise should allow it. To the contrary, others and I feel this practice is a contradiction of our individual rights and is a moral outrage.

Cost-related goals can be the most difficult to achieve. More cost does not imply more quality. We hear statements from hospitals and physician groups claiming they produce the highest quality and best patient outcomes at the lowest cost. Over decades, the American health care system has had limited success with a variety of models to produce this combination. In the comparison of US outcomes in Chapter 6, it is clear other countries produce better outcomes, at less cost. In a world of scarce resources, economists preach the goal of maximizing output through efficient utilization. Resources inefficiently expended for health care could be used to improve the standard of living in other ways.

It sounds simplistic, but the overriding goal should be for Americans to be as healthy as they can be. I like to refer to this as *health assurance*. For those with illnesses, this means they are doing and receiving all they need to maintain the highest quality of life possible, even with their illnesses. It also means they have easy access to providers they feel will address their needs in a timely manner, with quality and expertise. For people who are relatively healthy, it means they are receiving the support and monitoring they need to stay healthy. We tend to be overly focused on health care *insurance*, which is a structure, or subgoal, and not an overarching goal. Certainly, health assurance for all would first require health care *insurance* for all, including those with preexisting illnesses. Health assurance is the goal, and health care insurance is one means to reaching that goal. However, treating health care insurance as the only approach is a case of not seeing the forest through the trees. As we design the best American health care system, we should work backward from the goal of health assurance as we decide on system elements. The change process clearly should aim for the goal of producing high-quality health care at the lowest possible cost for all Americans.

CHAPTER 9

The Complexity of Balancing Affordability, Risk, and Access

Every American has choices for health care insurance. But each may be challenged to understand risks, affordability, and access when it comes to both private and public plans. Too many people are faced with complex options, testing their ability to adequately protect themselves and their loved ones. This is the challenge of health assurance. Some say a single-payer system would solve the problem by making Medicare available to everyone. Others advocate for continuation of the employer-based, private insurance model we have today, with a myriad of plans offered in the private sector by both for-profit companies and nonprofit organizations. As presently constituted, both models fail to guarantee health assurance. Too many of us are at risk of making wrong or inadequate choices.

Private Plans

Employees are torn and confused as they try to understand their choices. When illness hits, too often one is faced with surprise costs and limitations that weren't understood at the time the plan was chosen. Alternatively, many people choose a plan based on affordability, and they understand the possible negative consequences but just hope they do not get sick, or that when they do, the care they need will be covered.

Employees enjoying a health care insurance plan as a benefit are typically faced with choosing from a few plans their employer has decided to offer. This decision has significant economic consequences for the employer. The cost of all plans has risen over time, to represent an average 2019 national cost of $7,188 for an individual plan and $20,576 for a family plan (*2019 Employer Health Benefits Survey*, Henry J. Kaiser Family Foundation, September 25, 2019). An employer can design or redesign a plan to mitigate the impact to its bottom line. The specific options require employees to share in the higher cost.

There are three general ways an employer may pass the higher cost onto employees:

1. **Through the coinsurance formula.** If the total premium increases, and the formula requires employees to pay a stated percentage of the total premium (e.g., 25 percent), the employee automatically picks up that percentage of the increase. The employer, of course, could also decide to raise the percentage. There are other possible ways to set the coinsurance, and it could be as simple as a fixed dollar amount.

2. **Increase deductibles and co-payments.** For example, increase the out-of-pocket payment for a hospitalization from $500 to $1,500, and increase the co-payment for an emergency room visit from $100 to $200. A higher emergency room co-payment may influence employees to seek a cheaper alternative, such as a visit to a doctor or urgent care clinic. Prescription drug coverage can be changed to raise out-of-pocket payments for higher-cost drugs, or exclude certain expensive drugs from coverage altogether.

3. **Offer plans such as HMOs and PPOs.** These plans have a limited network of providers, as well as gatekeeper rules requiring preapproval for certain provider services. As a rule of thumb, the more limited the panel of providers in a plan, the less expensive the total premium. Hospitals and physician groups, being exclusive within a small panel, are likely to negotiate lower prices for their services if they can expect a higher volume of patients.

As several plans are offered with varying combinations of cost elements, employees are faced with complex choices. They must pick the plan with the right balance of affordability, risk, and access. The least costly coinsurance options usually present the highest financial risk. Employees wage rates may dictate the choice to have the lowest coinsurance amount deducted from their paychecks. This plan may put them at risk, should a family member get sick and trigger large co-payments and deductibles. It may also limit access to less preferable doctors and hospitals, or ones located a long distance from home.

As of 2018, there were still 27.9 million nonelderly Americans without health care insurance. The Kaiser Family Foundation's Issue Brief ("Key Facts About the Uninsured Population," December 13, 2018), commented on the *2018 American Community Survey*, where it was found that 72 percent of uninsured nonelderly Americans were in families with at least one person working full time, and typically with low income. No health care insurance was in place for them, because either their employers did not offer plans, or the plans offered were unaffordable. An article by Reed Abelson (*New York Times*, updated September 30, 2019) has a sub-headline: "A relentless rise in premiums and deductibles is putting insurance out of reach for many workers, especially those with low incomes." It reports on a twenty-seven-year-old woman in Washington, DC, with a heart condition, who considered the opportunity to move from a part-time job to full time in order to qualify for health care insurance. Instead, she quit her job and applied for Medicaid, when she learned her out-of-pocket costs would be at least $1,200 a month, an amount equal to double what she had left over after paying for rent and utilities. She began doing side jobs to keep her income low enough to qualify for Medicaid.

Stories abound, describing how workers with health care insurance decide to forgo medical care and needed drugs because they cannot afford the out-of-pocket deductibles and co-payments. Other disturbing stories tell about cancer patients needing drugs that cost as much as $150,000 a year and are covered by their plans at a minimal percentage—or not at all. This situation applies to Medicare Part D plans, as well as employer plans.

My late wife, Judy, passed away from cancer in October 2016. She was sixty-nine, and we were married for forty-seven years. She died a day after our first grandchild was born. There was a chemo drug available to treat her abdominal cancer, at an annual cost of $168,000. Her plan D coverage required us to pay a deductible of $5,000 in the first month, and $700 a month, thereafter. Our combined annual after-tax income, at the time, was about $90,000. This presented some financial hardship for us, but not nearly as much as for someone with less income. After paying the $5,000, she was only on the drug for one week, before having to discontinue it due to multiple side effects. The next possibility was a drug in clinical trial, but she never became healthy enough to start it.

Oncologists have coined a now-common term called "financial toxicity." It refers to the additional physical and mental effects that stem from anxiety over the financial burdens of a cancer diagnosis, which are mainly due to drug costs and the inability to continue in a job.

In our private, employer-based system, each employer decides what health care insurance is offered and at what cost to employees. There is clearly not equality in health assurance. Depending on where employees work, they face differences in affordability, access, health risk, and cost risk, compared to others. One of the worst cases is when an employee cannot afford the required coinsurance and chooses to be uninsured. Only 26 percent of employers have a coinsurance formula based on a sliding scale for income. Otherwise, everyone in the workplace pays the same dollar amount, and the only option for lesser coinsurance is to choose a cheaper plan with higher risks and less access. And since employees have an open enrollment period each year, the choices change in terms of cost and access, and employees must make new decisions.

Medicare

Medicare options require similar balancing of affordability, risk, and access. Traditional Medicare Part A, for inpatient hospital care, is free. But it has a deductible for a hospital stay and co-payments of 20 percent for services received while hospitalized. Medicare Part B, for outpatient services, has a 2021 premium of $148.50 for individual incomes below $88,000, and rises by income level on a sliding scale. Even after paying this premium, there are required co-payments, varying by type of service. In order to cover the payment gaps in both Parts A and B, there are Medigap and Medicare Advantage plans from private insurers for an additional premium. Prescription drug coverage under Part D is available through many different private plans, with various premiums and out-of-pocket costs.

There is significant financial burden and risk to low-income Medicare enrollees. Imagine a couple relying principally on annual Social Security, with a gross income of $35,000 and an after-tax (net) income of $32,500. The numbers here are taken from the "2021 Medicare Monthly Premiums" chart found under "Medicare" in Chapter 5. The couple could choose Traditional Medicare Parts A, B, and D, and each pay $148.50 per month for Part B and $41 for Part D. The total of $379/month is 14 percent of their monthly net income of $2,708. If they become ill, they are vulnerable to co-payments and deductibles. There is a $1,484 deductible for one hospitalization. Part D prescription drug plans typically have a $445 annual deductible, as well as co-payments after the deductible is fulfilled. They could avoid most deductibles and co-payments under Parts A and B by purchasing a Medigap plan at $152/month. The new monthly health plan premiums, including Plan D, would total $683, or 25.2 percent of their monthly net income. This example is pertinent since 26 percent of households with a householder age sixty-five or older had a gross annual income of $35,000 or less in 2016, and 38 percent had a gross annual income of $50,000 or less ("2017 Profile of Older Americans," The Administration for Community Living, US Department of Health and Human Services, April 2018).

An alternative for the couple would be to still pay $148.50 each for Part B and a premium of $21 each per month for an Advantage plan which includes prescription coverage. The total of $339 per month is the least expensive option, but the risks are threefold:

1. There will still be co-payments and deductibles. The premium of $21 is an average. A higher-priced plan could be purchased to reduce required co-payments and deductibles.

2. Advantage plans operate like an HMO or PPO, where pre-approvals are required. There are a multitude of reported stories on denials to seniors with significant health issues.

3. The network of providers is typically limited and may not include an enrollee's preferred hospitals and doctors. It may instead include providers located at an inconvenient distance.

It is no wonder that surveys and stories report serious hardships for low-income seniors on Medicare. An article in the Greenville News ("People on Medicare Struggle More with Medicare Bills than Seniors in Other Countries," February 11, 2018) tells of a seventy-eight-year-old man working as a driver to pay his medical bills. He was diagnosed with lung cancer two years earlier and said he was spending $10,000 a year on medical costs despite being on Medicare. There is no cap on out-of-pocket spending under Part

D, and once annual drug costs exceed $6,350, patients are required to pay 5 percent. This would amount to $7,500 for a cancer drug costing $150,000 for a year's dosage.

Medicare in its present form does not offer health assurance for all Medicare-eligible people. Seniors will choose what they can afford, with varying degrees of financial vulnerability. As in employer-based, private-sector plans, there are differences of opportunity for health assurance, principally based on income.

Medicaid

Now I will cover Medicaid, where eligibility is for those with low incomes. Provider pricing is legislated with no negotiation. Payments to providers are the lowest, compared to private insurance and Medicare. There are many doctors who do not accept Medicaid patients. Government-supported community health centers are often the only accessible places for primary care and other health services for those with Medicaid. Doctors at these centers altruistically accept salaries less than market rate. It is all very simple: those with Medicaid have only this one choice for a plan. The only alternative is to be uninsured.

Studies find that about 30 percent of physicians do not accept new patients covered by Medicaid. This was a finding in a well-known 2011 study. There are wide differences around the average by state. There have been a few surveys since then, and they roughly approximate the 2011 study findings.

Access to providers is important, because most states have now accepted Medicaid expansion under the Affordable Care Act. States set their own Medicaid provider payment rates, and there appears to be a correlation between provider participation in Medicaid and the rates paid in each state. Medicaid is just one more segment of the fragmented American health care system.

Surprise Billing

Beginning around 2019, there has been discussion in Congress and in state legislatures on how to protect people from a phenomenon called "surprise billing." This is about patients accessing health care services, thinking the services are in their health care plan's network of covered providers, and then being billed for all or part of the services. It can happen for those covered in both private and government plans. An individual may go to a hospital covered by their health care insurance plan, but then receive a surprise bill for ancillary or physician services by a clinician in an independent provider group that is under contract with the hospital, but does not have a contract with the individual's health care insurance plan. The provider could be an anesthesiologist, pathologist, surgeon, emergency physician, or physical therapist, among others. Here are two stories from *Consumer Reports* ("Member Stories: Medical Bills," consumerreports.org/stories?questionnaireId=14 and "Surprise Medical Bills," https//advocacy.consumerreports. org/research/surprise-medical-bills):

The morning of Misty's C-Section the couple was told the scheduled anesthesiologist was unavailable. The out-of-network doctor that replaced him charged $15,000. "We had no option to reschedule. It would have been a risk to the baby's life," says Robert. "We had no control over this situation."

I turned a tractor over on myself and broke my tibia. It was a compound fracture. When the ambulance arrived, I asked them to take me to a hospital I knew was in network. They stated they had to take me to a level three trauma hospital. When they told me what hospital they were taking me to I was relieved as it was an in-network hospital. Six months later I received a bill from a nurse practitioner for $3,709 for emergency room care. They told me the doctor I saw in the emergency room was not in network and that I was responsible for the bill. How is anyone to know what doctor is going to see them in a hospital when they get there and then know or be able to check if they are in network or no? If the hospital is in network, then the doctors should be as well.

There is another type of surprise billing called "balance billing." A health care insurance plan may cover "reasonable and customary" charges from an out-of-network physician, but the physician may consider the amount to be less than her or his usual charge and bill the patient for the difference.

Surprise billing is a fairly common experience. In their February 2020 Tracking Poll ("Data Note: Public Worries About and Experience with Surprise Medical Bills," kff.org, Feb 28, 2020), the Kaiser Family Foundation found that among insured adults ages eighteen to sixty-four, 33 percent had received an unexpected medical bill over the prior two years. A third of this group said the bill was $1,000 or more. Among those with annual household incomes of less than $40,000, 72 percent answered they could not afford a $500 bill.

Notes from the COVID-19 Pandemic

The worldwide COVID-19 pandemic has accelerated a number of trends. Things like online shopping, working from home using virtual communication, telemedicine, online education, and TV streaming have quickly become commonplace. Additionally, millions of people have faced new challenges in our employer-based health care insurance model, exposing its inadequacies. The hope is that through these new experiences, so many who felt well-protected before will now have the expanded understanding and empathy needed to propel change.

People who never lost a job before have been in a panic to find an affordable alternative to their employer-based health care plan. Some have family members in the middle of receiving care for a chronic condition, illness, cancer, and even pregnancy. These people have sought, for the first time, to understand how to apply for Medicaid and subsidized plans on exchanges created under the Affordable Care Act.

Those who experienced symptoms of the virus, while continuing in private plans or Medicare, faced barriers and costs as they pursued testing and care. Many experienced high co-payments, surprise billing, and access limitations for the first time. In some cases, those with symptoms, being uninsured or in plans with high deductibles, have decided not to pursue care because of the expense. This has worked against our national goal to identify everyone with COVID-19 so they could be quarantined and have their contacts traced. Those with low income have been the most vulnerable, with disproportionate representation in the ranks of the uninsured and underinsured. They have also been more likely to contract the virus due to living in dense neighborhoods and continuing to work in low-paid jobs deemed to be essential. Such jobs include nurse aides in hospitals and nursing homes, warehouse workers, and grocery store clerks. These jobs are often held by Black and Brown people, among other minority populations. Given their health disparities and lack of access to health care, it is not surprising that these populations are unequally represented among COVID-19 deaths. Lev Facher reported, "Black people represent 6 percent of Wisconsin's population—but account for nearly half of the state's coronavirus deaths. Black people, similarly, account for two-thirds of Chicago's deaths despite constituting only one-third of its population. Across the country, the story is the same: Covid-19 is killing people of color, particularly Black people, at staggeringly disproportionate rates" ("Nine ways Covid-19 may forever upend the U.S. health care industry," STAT, May 19. 2020).

The states and the federal government have scrambled to apply band-aids, such as requiring insurers not to charge for COVID-19 testing and reducing waiting periods and processing times for Medicaid and plans available on state exchanges under the Affordable Care Act. Some of these fixes have worked, and some have run into other snags. All of this has been unnecessary in most other developed nations, because they have universal health care. At any moment in time, whether there is a pandemic, a recession, or any disruption in the individual lives of their citizens, all continue in the national health plan without interruption.

A CNN story ("She was asked to pay thousands for her coronavirus treatment, he got a free ride. She's American. He's Italian," CNN.com, Ivana Kottasova, Tami Luhby and Valentina Di, May 1, 2020) juxtaposes the experiences of an American and an Italian, who both tested positive for COVID-19. They each were brought to a hospital and admitted for intensive treatment. The Italian was unemployed at the time, but that did not affect his health care coverage, and he paid nothing toward his care under the Italian system of universal coverage. The American was covered by a health care insurance plan from her husband's employer. At the time of the CNN report, she was receiving bills for her ambulance ride ($2,000) and paying hundreds of dollars for doctor visits at the hospital and prescription drugs. The insurance company said they were waiving out-of-pocket costs for certain employer plans, but not all. She had not yet heard anything from them on a waiver of her bills.

At this writing, COVID-19 cases continue to grow on a daily basis, reaching large numbers. Several measures have finally been put in place by governments (federal and state) and insurers to alleviate the financial burden of uncovered medical bills. However, much anxiety has been created in the interim, people are still not educated on what relief they can expect, there are gaps and variations from state to state, and much effort is being expended to apply for and process financial support.

Our System Cries out for Change

In a *Boston Globe* series, Elizabeth Rosenthal catalogs the experience of Americans in our health care system ("Choosing a plan from the impossible health care maze," December 2, 2019). The descriptions are done so well that paraphrasing would not do them justice. Here are a few:

In this highly partisan political moment, there's one issue that nearly every American can agree on: Our health care system is a mess and in need of dramatic overhaul.

That's not just because it is absurdly expensive compared to other developed countries. It's also because the system is so dauntingly complex.

That complexity derives in large part because the health care system has been driven significantly by profit, rather than by measures of health. There are countless providers, companies, consultants, and intermediaries trying to get their piece of the $3.5 trillion pie that is US health care...

That has led to a maze-like system—with twists and turns and barriers and blind alleys and incomprehensible signposts—that ordinary people are expected to navigate.

We say American patients should be happy because our system gives consumers choices. We tell people that to benefit they just need to be smarter shoppers. What we are really telling them is to perform the impossible.

How can they choose an insurance policy when there are endless permutations involving personal budget calculations and modeling that would defy a post-doc in economics? For each policy, there's an in-network deductible and an out-of-network deductible, overlapping for the family and each individual. There are co-pays and co-insurance (yes, they're different), as well as an annual maximum personal out-of-pocket outlay (which may not include some of the above).

Likewise, how to choose between a PPO and an HMO, especially when the PPO network may be—or may become—so narrow during the term of the policy that it affords little or no choice of doctors...

The system is rigged against patients—thanks largely to its opacity and complexity. Insurance plans list an array of covered services but then can refuse to precertify a prescribed treatment or decide it was not medically necessary and deny coverage after the fact. For example, a patient goes to the emergency room with chest pain, which turns out to be just a pulled muscle. So, in retrospect, it wasn't an emergency. Coverage denied!

The current complexity is an outgrowth of countless decisions over the past 30 years, many of which sounded logical at the time, but which grew out of financial considerations. All the players are effectively licensed to reach into our wallets when they can't get the money they want from each other.

As prices spiraled upward, insurers (backed by economists) imposed co-payments and co-insurance so patients would have "skin in the game," to encourage them to use health care more sparingly, more wisely. But with prices in medicine now so high, the skin-in-the-game theory now means many patients live with debilitating symptoms, delay needed treatment, or don't get treated at all.

In one study, 1 in 4 diabetics reported taking less insulin than prescribed because of costs. Another found that one-fifth of cardiac patients with "financial hardship" cut back on both food and medicines...

Americans trying to be smart shoppers are understandably confused about navigating the open enrollment season, as they are doing currently. And just when they have figured it out for one year, they have to do it all over again. The odds of success are small.

The American health care system is overly complex, risky, and financially challenging for a large number of us. There is inequality of access and cost. We fall short on our goal of health assurance for all. Outcomes in the American health care system are behind the rest of the world. Politicians propose a variety of solutions, but the conversation is narrowly focused on changing structures. The change process must begin with goals and end with the structural design needed to achieve them. Two things are very clear: there is a dire need for simplification and a great need for equality of opportunity for health assurance.

CHAPTER 10

Alternatives for the American Health Care System

When evaluating the array of alternative designs for the American health care system, there should be a focus on five goals in the quest for health assurance for all:

1. Health care insurance for all. In spite of the passage of the Affordable Care Act, there are nearly 28 million Americans without health care insurance. Although this is a significant reduction from the 47 million uninsured in 2010, we still have a way to go.

2. Equality of coverage, access, and choices for all, regardless of income, and enrollment without regard for any preexisting illnesses or diseases.

3. Simplification.

4. High-quality care, positioning the United States as a world leader in outcomes.

5. Cost reduction or stabilization.

The design options are:

1. Eliminate all private health plans and become a single-payer system, with Americans of all ages enrolled, perhaps, in Medicare—"Medicare for All."

2. Retain the private health plan system as we know it, and expand the Affordable Care Act to reduce the uninsured population to zero.

3. Add Medicare as a public option, alongside private plans.

4. Make changes in the pricing and payment methodology for both private and government health plans, to make them more cost-effective.

Each is discussed here, along with observations on how they do or do not fulfill desired goals. Of course, there are favorable characteristics in each, which could be blended to create other models. Some may not fulfill all goals but could be implemented on a timeline, in a transition to the ultimate model.

Medicare for All: Single-Payer System
This option has a unique advantage, with regard to cost. The cost of processing claims and administration would be less than 5 percent,

compared to 10 to 20 percent for private insurance plans. The simple reason is economy of scale. With about 60 million Americans currently using Medicare, the average cost for administrative overhead and claims processing can be kept low. In spite of low overhead costs, survey data shows that recipients and providers are pleased with Medicare's service and timely claims processing.

Under traditional Medicare, in both Part A and Part B, there is access to all doctors, hospitals, and other participating providers, without the requirement for preapproval. Nearly all providers participate in Medicare. Restriction to designated providers exists in a number of private supplementary (Medigap) plans and Medicare Advantage plans. These plans are purchased in the private sector, for the purpose of covering the deductible and co-payment gaps in Parts A and B. In order to achieve the goal of health assurance and open access to all providers, such restrictions could be removed by legislation. Alternatively, all private plans could be eliminated and replaced with access to all providers, as exists now under Parts A and B.

Currently, Medicare is unaffordable for many Americans. There is a required premium for participation in Part B, which increases with income on a scale but is set at a 2021 minimum of $148.50. To meet the affordability goal, it would be necessary to eliminate this premium altogether, or have the premium not apply for those with incomes below a determined amount. In addition, the premium for Part B tops off at incomes of $500,000 or more and could be raised for incomes higher than this level. Traditional Medicare has deductibles and co-payments. To meet the affordability goals, it would be necessary to eliminate them, at least for low-income individuals. This would then relieve low-income enrollees of the expense of purchasing a supplementary plan or a Medicare Advantage plan. It would also be necessary to deal similarly with Part D, for prescription drugs. In the interest of simplification, it may be best to eliminate all the Medicare parts, as well as supplementary and Advantage plans. There would be one set of comprehensive coverage, applicable to all, but with enrollee premiums based on a more reasonable income scale than currently in place.

This alternative would be better characterized as "single-payer" rather than Medicare (in its current form) for All. As described above, the rules and coverage under Medicare are not necessarily the right framework if we move to universal coverage and eliminate private sector health care insurance. In a single-payer system, the government is the sole insurer with provider prices and coverage rules dictated by legislation. The question, here, is whether the government would legislate rules and prices that best address our health assurance goals. This is perhaps the largest objection to single-payer. Will politicians succumb, over time, to other costly priorities and reduce coverage? Will the same pressures cause them to legislate unacceptable payments for the care doctors provide, discouraging entry into the field and ultimately causing shortages that impact access to timely and conveniently located care?

Expansion of the Affordable Care Act

In order to achieve the five goals, our government could legislate specific requirements to address some of them, but within the context of our existing health care system—with its mixture of employer-based health care plans and government programs. This is essentially the purpose of the Affordable Care Act. However, changes must still be made to expand health care insurance, reduce the 27.5 million Americans who are still uninsured, and meet other goals.

Here is what is in place through the ACA, passed in 2010, along with ideas for changes to meet the goal of health assurance:

1. The Affordable Care Act requires health care insurance plans to accept all enrollees, including those with preexisting conditions. Before the act was passed, most states allowed plans to deny coverage to those with preexisting conditions, or to charge them higher premiums. This is a key provision of the ACA. There have been lawsuits aiming to nullify this provision of the ACA and give back states' rights to set their own rules on denying coverage for pre-existing conditions.

2. In most states, uninsured families and individuals at or below 138 percent of the poverty level are eligible for Medicaid, at no cost. Under the ACA, the federal government will pay states 90 percent of the cost to expand Medicaid, to include eligibility up to the 138 percent threshold. In 2012, a US Supreme Court decision gave states the right to refuse these payments and not expand Medicaid to more uninsured residents. As of November 2020, there were still twelve states not providing expanded coverage. In these states, the median income threshold for Medicaid eligibility is 41 percent of the poverty level for families, and zero for individuals. This leaves uninsured people with income up to 138 percent of the poverty level, who could be eligible if their states accepted the Medicaid expansion under the ACA. This would have to change for the "insurance for all" goal to be met.

Even if there were full Medicaid expansion to all the states, the Medicaid program, itself, fails on an important goal: equality of access to all providers. As explained, the legislated payment rates for provider services to Medicaid enrollees are so low that many doctors do not agree to accept Medicaid patients. These patients are largely limited to community health centers for care, and they may have to travel long distances for specialty care. The only answer for change is obviously to legislate higher Medicaid payment rates for providers.

3. As shown in Chapter 5, a couple in Pennsylvania, with no children and a combined annual gross income of $68,960, is expected to afford to pay 9.83 percent (or $6,679) of their income for a silver plan on Pennsylvania's ACA exchange. Their income is 400 percent of the poverty level—the maximum income for which the ACA allows a tax credit for a family of that size. The full cost of a silver plan is $14,400, and they are eligible for a tax credit of $7,621, leaving them with a payment of $6,679. A silver plan has the financial risk of high deductibles and co-payments. The couple could reduce their risk by putting the $7,621 tax credit toward the gold or platinum plan, which have lower potential out-of-pocket costs. But that would put a bigger dent in their budget.

    The ACA tax credit table allows tax credits for incomes up to 400 percent of the poverty level, with the expected percentage of income to be paid toward a plan at each tier (bronze, silver, gold, platinum). Out-of-pocket deductibles and co-payments are lower, as one proceeds up the tiers to the platinum plan. Studies show that millions of Americans remain uninsured, because they find the ACA tax credit numbers and calculations unaffordable, or they are not eligible, because their income is above the limit of 400 percent of the poverty level. Modifications to the ACA rules could make a difference in reducing the number of uninsured. There are three suggested approaches:

- Expand eligibility to those with incomes above 400 percent of the poverty level, perhaps to 600 percent.

- Reduce the percentages of income defined to be affordable at each level. In the above example, the Pennsylvania couple might decide to purchase a plan if their expected contribution was reduced from 9.83 percent of their income to 8 percent.

- The high out-of-pocket requirements at the silver level are significant, and the dollars of affordability are calculated by multiplying the income percentage of affordability times the full cost a silver plan. The tax credit is the difference between that dollar amount and the full premium. This could be changed so that the affordability percentage is multiplied times the gold plan premium, to yield a higher tax credit.

These suggestions may seem overly complicated. In simple form, the approach would be to improve affordability by granting greater tax credits toward the purchase of health care insurance.

4. Major changes in pricing and payment methodologies clearly impact the goal of reducing costs. They also bring the opportunity to divert financial resources toward other goals. As we have seen, the United States spends a much higher portion of GDP on health care than other developed countries, and most of them have universal health care coverage. Savings from cost reductions could be used toward achieving other goals, including health care for all. Also, a new provider services payment methodology could lead to better outcomes, by incentivizing providers for improvements in wellness and quality.

    Currently, our fee-for-service system rewards doctors and other providers for doing more. So the sicker the patients, the greater the needed medical services and the revenue they produce. A fairly new system is beginning to demonstrate success. Hospital systems, with their employed physician groups, are forming accountable care organizations, or ACOs, and contracting with health care insurers and government programs under a "capitated" arrangement, rather than on a fee-for-service basis. As a group, they accept an annual flat fee per patient, called a per-capita payment, to cover any and all services provided within their group. The group essentially puts its income at risk but has the opportunity for gain by expending less than the annual capitated payments. The incentive is to keep patients well, with less need for hospitalizations, surgeries, and other medical services. Doctors are motivated to stay in close touch with patients to ensure compliance with necessary care after leaving the hospital so they will not get sicker and return soon after being discharged.

Of course, the danger of this approach is that providers will withhold necessary tests and treatments, to retain more of the capitated payments for themselves. This did happen in the early '90s, with simpler capitation methodologies. Today there are careful design and tracking methods to prevent this. There is extensive monitoring of performance measures of quality and outcomes, with corresponding penalties and rewards. The sophistication of "health care informatics" makes this possible. The good news is that the ACO model can be applied to whatever combination of private and public health care insurance plans we design for a new American health care system.

5. Roughly half of all Americans receive their health care insurance coverage through employers. The ACA includes a provision to expand this coverage, by imposing tax penalties on employers with fifty or more full-time equivalent employees who do not provide health care insurance with certain minimum provisions to 95 percent full-time equivalent employees. The tax penalty in 2021 is $2,700 per full-time employee (defined as working thirty hours or more). Employers' plans must be "affordable" and pay 60 percent of covered health care expenses. In 2021, the definition of affordable is that an employee's share of the premium (coinsurance) is no more than 9.83 percent of that person's income. This provision continues to be in effect, despite a number of legal challenges. The affordability percentage is the same as the maximum expected percentage under the tax credit section of the ACA and was set as such to

minimize plan enrollment through the state exchanges, rather than in employer plans.

There is not clear evidence on the degree to which this provision has reduced the ranks of the uninsured. The limitations in the design are evident. Employers with less than fifty full-time employees are exempt from the mandate. Further, paying only 60 percent of covered services leaves a lot of risk for out-of-pocket payments. Yet it was one of many elements of the ACA that addressed goals of affordability and reducing the number of uninsured Americans. The rules could be modified for more success on these goals.

6. The ACA initially included the requirement for everyone to have health care insurance, even those with incomes too high to be eligible for Medicaid or tax credits. This has been referred to as the individual mandate. Those who opt not to buy insurance may be healthy individuals who are self-employed, employees who do not wish to select a plan offered by their employer, or workers whose employers do not offer health care insurance. The purpose of the individual mandate was to reduce overall private health care insurance premiums, through larger enrollment by individuals whose premium payments would exceed payouts for their medical services. The individual mandate was ruled by the US Supreme Court to be unconstitutional and eliminated as part of the 2017 Tax Reform Act.

The ACA was a comprehensive attempt to address goals of health assurance for all, within the framework of a predominately private, employer-based health care system. It successfully reduced the number of uninsured Americans from 47 million to 27.5 million. So an option for the future is to retain the employer-based framework and legislate further improvements on a path to fulfilling all the goals of health assurance for all.

Medicare as a Public Option

In the political debate on health care coverage, there are proponents of offering Medicare as an option to people under age sixty-five. Taking this route could place Medicare as a choice, alongside private plans offered by employers and for purchase in the marketplace. It is proposed by some as a possible way station to eventual Medicare for All. Those now opposed to Medicare for All, and desirous of keeping their private plans, would be able to see firsthand the value and cost of Medicare.

It is not clear what a Medicare plan would look like in terms of design and cost for those under age sixty-five. Would it be identical to its current form, with Parts A and B and the availability of supplemental and Medicare Advantage plans offered by private insurers? Would there be access to all providers, with no network limitations? The design arguably should take the structural form of the private-sector plans with which it would compete. The cost for all private and public health plans is derived mainly from the claims experience, or usage, of plan participants. The government's cost of Medicare is determined by the usage of an elderly population. Would the claims experience of seniors be combined with the experiences of those under sixty-five, to calculate a premium? The principal cost advantages of Medicare are its economies of scale and lower pricing of provider services.

Designing a new Medicare plan, as an offering to those under age sixty-five, simply mimics what already exists in the private sector and does not necessarily fulfill goals of affordability, simplicity, and more access. The political process, coupled with private insurance lobbying, may take a very long time. Besides that, the result might be no better than our current employer-based system, which needs reform to reach desired goals. It may only be a costly intermediate step to design and implement a new system, and time could be lost in the movement toward real reform. At this writing, the states of Washington and Colorado are going through the stages of implementing a state-run public option. This is a bottom-up process and could be very costly.

Whatever health care system model we choose for the future, it must include financial rewards and penalties for behaviors and activities related to lifelong wellness. Americans score low on wellness indicators compared to other countries. The one stand-out indicator is obesity and its relationship to diabetes, heart disease, and other conditions. If the goals of universal, affordable, and accessible health care become a shared financial burden through the tax system, each person must be held accountable for living a healthy lifestyle and taking preventive measures, such as annual physicals and cancer screenings. Many employer plans do have these provisions, but as individuals change employers over their careers, employers have limited ways to reap the cost benefits of a healthy workforce over the long term. A single-payer plan could offer a consistent set of incentives, both positive and negative, and an opportunity to achieve cost savings from lifelong wellness behavior.

CHAPTER 11

Impacts, Barriers, Complexity, and Possibilities

My main message for the public and policymakers is to focus on goals, rather than structures. Our current system is fraught with inequality. The degree of health assurance varies by income. Those who can afford high premiums, large coinsurance deductions from their paychecks, deductibles, and co-payments experience less financial risk and have access to providers of their choice. Low and middle income individuals who are working may choose to be uninsured because they cannot afford the coinsurance required for participation in their employers' plans. Those who take a risk and leave themselves vulnerable by staying uninsured, or by choosing plans with large out-of-pocket payments, do not seek primary and preventive care. This leads to costs falling on others, when uninsured Americans resort to only episodic care, usually through a hospital emergency room, and do not have the ability to pay their bills.

Those whose only choice is Medicaid under the Affordable Care Act have their access limited to a small number of providers, mostly at community health centers. Low-income seniors on Medicare may not be able to afford the Part B premium and the supplementary plan to cover the gaps in Medicare coverage. They can enroll in a low-cost Medicare Advantage plan as an alternative but would be limited to a specified network of providers and be at risk for high out-of-pocket costs.

Inequality of health assurance is endemic to our employer-based health care system. We are subject to our employer's decision on whether health care insurance will be offered, the plans offered, and how much we pay out-of-pocket when we use the plan. Different employers may have different premiums for identical plans, because they have a different mix of healthy and sick employees. Health plans adjust annual premiums based on the prior year's claims experience or plan usage. All employees may be faced with higher coinsurance because a few of their coworkers had high-cost care in the prior year.

Once the details of our American health care system are understood, its complexity becomes painfully clear. Imagine the circumstances of a family losing health care insurance because of a job loss. It becomes a major task to find coverage that is affordable, with access to providers of choice, and to quickly try to understand complicated eligibility and rules for Medicaid or tax credits under the ACA. Imagine this happening suddenly, to millions of Americans, when the COVID-19 pandemic hit. Imagine an employee, during an employer's open enrollment period, struggling to comprehend the affordability of premiums, risks of out-of-pocket payments, and differences in provider networks within HMOs, PPOs, and other plan types. Imagine a senior citizen trying, each year, to choose the right and affordable combination from Medicare Parts A, B, and D and supplemental plans, and trying to determine whether a Medicare Advantage plan is the best alternative. Imagine any American individual or family realizing the only affordable option available is to be uninsured.

Most other developed countries have single-payer systems covering all citizens. The cost of their systems is paid by higher taxes. The government makes decisions on coverage and prices paid for provider services. As discussed in Chapter 6, health outcomes in countries with single-payer systems are better than ours.

So why are we different? I will offer my view. It begins with the sacredness of the American economic system, which is based on competition. We largely believe that freely operating markets produce the best results for our citizens, and the government should not intervene. I would argue that if our goal is health assurance for all, this is not possible in competitive markets. It just has not happened. One can possibly argue that we can achieve the lowest health care insurance costs when private insurance plans are allowed to compete. This could very well be the case, but the market does not fulfill the goals of health assurance for all, as described in this book. If we stay with our employer-based system, it will be necessary for the government to intervene, to achieve goals of equal affordability and access. The Affordable Care Act was legislated for this purpose, though over the years there have been a number of attempts in the courts to find it unconstitutional. At this writing, there is such a case pending before the US Supreme Court.

The large government cost for a single-payer system would translate into higher taxes, as argued strongly by opponents. As an offset, premium costs could be eliminated for everyone, including employers. Co-payments and deductibles could go away. The math would determine whether there could be a full offset, but it is unlikely. A number of studies demonstrate different degrees of offset, based on a variety of assumptions.

Continuation and expansion of the Affordable Care Act within the employer-based system also would come with costs. How far we expand it to achieve health assurance goals will also be dependent on the public's tolerance for tax increases.

Our decision to move to single-payer or an expansion/reform of our employer-based system will largely be based on trust. Do we trust the government, employers, or a combination of both to make the right decisions on what health care system best produces health care assurance for our citizens? A large number of people say they like their current health care insurance plans and do not want to change them. It may be that the country is not ready to embrace our government as the single payer. It may be necessary to make this transition over time. Meanwhile, we can continue with reforms under an expansion of the Affordable Care Act, which eventually would move us to a single-payer system.

The information presented herein will not only be beneficial to readers as they make their choices on health care insurance, but also serve as a call to action for Americans to advocate for health assurance for all. This can be done in many different ways. The easiest way is to be proactive in sharing knowledge and expressing opinions to friends and family. Going public is fairly easy, through social media and other internet vehicles such as blogs, podcasts, and participation in webinars. Newspaper op-eds and letters to the editor are obvious avenues. Politicians can be informed through emails and public forums. There is a dire need to take these actions, because so much misunderstanding surrounds the complex workings of the American health care system. Policymakers must be guided by public opinion. There is nothing worse than implementing a system that produces unintended results. Armed with knowledge, the electorate can be a driving force in steering policymakers in the right direction.

All Americans deserve access to affordable and high-quality health care. Unlike any other good or service available in our economy, health care is about life itself. As a country, we have a responsibility for the well-being of others, as well as ourselves. It will take moral courage to accept the changes necessary to achieve health assurance for all. Other, less wealthy nations have done so. Why can't we?

Bibliography

Abelson, Reed. "Employer Health Insurance Is Increasingly Unaffordable, Study Finds." *New York Times*, Sept 25, 2019. https://www.nytimes.com/2019/09/25/health/employer-health-insurance-cost.html

Administration for Community Living, US Department of Health and Human Services. "2017 Profile of Older Americans," Apr 2018. https://acl.gov/sites/default/files/Aging%20and%20Disability%20in%20America/2017OlderAmericansProfile.pdf

Agarwal, Sumit. "Physicians who refuse to accept Medicaid patients breach their contract with Society." STAT, Dec 28, 2017. https://www.statnews.com/2017/12/28/medicaid-physicians-social-contract/

Albrecht, Leslie. "Most major health insurers aren't charging patients for coronavirus treatment -but that doesn't mean it's free." Marketwatch.com, May 11, 2020. https://qz.com/1853315/the-cost-of-coronavirus-care-depends-on-where-americans-live/

Advisory Board. "The ACA boosted Medicaid payments for two years. But doctors were no more likely to take Medicaid patients, studies find." advisory.com, Jul 24, 2018. https://www.advisory.com/daily-briefing/2018/07/24/medicaid-payment

Allen, John R. and Darrell M. West, editors. "Reopening America: How to save Lives and Livelihoods." Brookings Institute, 2020. https://www.brookings.edu/wp-content/uploads/2020/05/Brookings-Reopening-America-FINAL.pdf

Altman, Drew. "Employer-based coverage is unaffordable for low-wage workers." Axios, Sep 26, 2019. https://www.axios.com/employer-based-coverage-is-unaffordable-for-low-wage-workers-f6855a5e-83ed-452e-825a-7ed966dd0f3b.html

Altman, Drew. "Health Care Costs as Much as a New Car." kff.org, Aug 23, 2019. https://www.kff.org/health-costs/perspective/health-care-costs-as-much-as-a-new-car/

Appleby, Julie. "COVID Catch 22: They Got A Big ER Bill Because Hospitals Couldn't Test For Virus." khn.org, Jul 7, 2020. https://khn.org/news/covid-catch-22-they-got-a-big-er-bill-because-hospitals-couldnt-test-for-virus/

Barua, Bacchus and Mackenzie Moir. "Comparing performance of Universal Health Care Countries, 2019." Fraser Institute, 2019. https://www.fraserinstitute.org/sites/default/files/comparing-health-care-countries-2019.pdf

Beers, Laura. "I've lived the difference between US and UK health care. Here's what I learned." CNN, Aug 7, 2019. https://www.cnn.com/2019/08/07/opinions/single-payer-healthcare-beers/index.html

Berchick, Edward R., Jessica Barnett and Rachel D. Upton. "Health Insurance Coverage in the United States: 2018 U.S. Census Bureau," Nov 8, 2019. https://www.census.gov/library/publications/2019/demo/p60-267.html

Biotechnology Innovation Organization. "How are prescription drug costs really determined?" drugcostfacts.org, 2020. https://www.drugcostfacts.org/prescription-drug-costs

Blumberg, Linda J. and John Holahan. "How would a Medicare buy-in and a public option be designed?" Urban Institute, Sep 2016. https://pnhp.org/news/how-would-a-medicare-buy-in-and-a-public-option-be-designed/

Boston Globe, "Choosing, Using, and Losing Health Care: A First-Aid Kit [4 part series]." December 2, 2019. https://www.bostonglobe.com/2019/12/02/opinion/choosing-using-losing-your-health-care-first-aid-kit/

Burns, Joseph, "As employers attempt to contain health insurance costs, workers in families struggle too." Association of Health Care Journalists, Nov 12, 2019. https://healthjournalism.org/blog/2019/11/as-employers-attempt-to-contain-health-insurance-costs-workers-and-families-struggle-too/

Cara, Anthony. "Missourians to vote on Medicaid Expansion as Crisis Leaves Millions Without Insurance." khn.org, Jul 30, 2020. https://khn.org/news/missourians-to-vote-on-medicaid-expansion-as-crisis-leaves-millions-without-insurance/

Christensen, Jen. "US life expectancy is still on the decline. Here's why." CNN, Nov 26, 2019. https://www.cnn.com/2019/11/26/health/us-life-expectancy-decline-study/index.html

Ciavaglia, Jo. "Buying health coverage in Pennsylvania next year? Here is the mostly good news." Bucks County Courier Times, Oct 15, 2020. https://www.buckscountycouriertimes.com/story/news/2020/10/15/pennie-insurance-exchange-health-insurance-pennsylvania-obamacare/3662439001/

Claxton, Gary, Bradley Sawyer and Cynthia Cox. "How affordability of healthcare varies by income among people with employer coverage." Peterson-KFF Health System Tracker, Apr 30, 2019. https://www.healthsystemtracker.org/brief/how-affordability-of-health-care-varies-by-income-among-people-with-employer-coverage/

Coble, John, "A Guide to Socialized Medicine in Other Countries and a Comparison to the American Healthcare System." Medium.com, Jul 29, 2019. https://medium.com/swlh/a-guide-to-socialized-medicine-in-other-countries-and-a-comparison-to-the-american-healthcare-f9450804c3ed

Collins, Sara R., David C. Radley and Jesse C. Baumgartner. "Trends in Employer Health Care Coverage, 2008- 2018: Higher Costs for Workers and Their Families" The Commonwealth Fund, Nov 21, 2019. https://www.commonwealthfund.org/publications/2019/nov/trends-employer-health-care-coverage-2008-2018

Consumer Reports. "Member Stories: Medical Bills." Consumerreports.org, 2020. https://www.consumerreports.org/stories?questionnaireId=14

Consumer Reports. "Surprise Medical Bills." advocacy.consumerreports.org. Nov 21, 2019. https://advocacy.consumerreports.org/research/surprise-medical-bills/

Cubanski, Juliette, Tricia Neuman, Anthony Damico and Karen Smith. "Medicare Beneficiaries' Out-of-Pocket Health Care Spending as a Share of Income Now and Projections for the Future." kff.org, Jan 26, 2018. https://www.kff.org/medicare/

report/medicare-beneficiaries-out-of-pocket-health-care-spending-as-a-share-of-income-now-and-projections-for-the-future/

Cubanski, Juliette and Anthony Damico. "Medicare Part D: A First Look at Medicare Prescription Drug Plans in 2021." Kaiser Family Foundation, Oct 19, 2020. https://www.kff.org/medicare/issue-brief/medicare-part-d-a-first-look-at-medicare-prescription-drug-plans-in-2021/

Cubanski, Juliette, Wyatt Koma, Anthony Damico and Tricia Neuman. "How Much Do Medicare Beneficiaries Spend Out of Pocket on Health Care?" kff.org, Nov 4, 2019. https://www.kff.org/medicare/issue-brief/how-much-do-medicare-beneficiaries-spend-out-of-pocket-on-health-care/

eHealth Medicare. "How Much Does a Medicare Supplement Insurance Plan Cost?" ehealthinsurance.com, 2020. https://www.ehealthinsurance.com/medicare/supplement-all/how-much-medicare-supplement-plans-cost

Epstein, Lita. "Pitfalls of Medicare Advantage Plans." Investopedia, Apr 14, 2020. https://www.investopedia.com/articles/personal-finance/010816/pitfalls-medicare-advantage-plans.asp

Facher, Lev. "Nine ways Covid-19 may forever upend the U.S. health care industry." STAT, May 19. 2020. https://www.statnews.com/2020/05/19/9-ways-covid-19-forever-upend-health-care/

Feke, Tanya, MD. "How Much Does Medicare Part D Cost?" Verywellhealth.com, Mar 20, 2020. https://www.verywellhealth.com/medicare-part-d-costs-4589863

Findley, Steven. "Health insurance Costs Crushing Many People Who don't Get federal Subsidies." khn.org, Dec 14, 2018. https://khn.org/news/health-insurance-costs-crushing-many-people-who-dont-get-federal-subsidies/

Frigand, Hannah. "On the frontline of the Health Care For All HelpLine." *Boston Globe*, Dec 9, 2019. https://www.bostonglobe.com/2019/12/09/opinion/frontline-health-care-all-helpline/

Fuglesten Biniek, Jeannie, Meredith Freed, Anthony Damico and Tricia Newman. "Medicare Advantage 2021 Spotlight: First Look." Kaiser Family Foundation, Oct 29, 2020. https://www.kff.org/medicare/issue-brief/medicare-advantage-2021-spotlight-first-look/

Gaffney, Adam, David Himmelstein and Steffie Woolhandler. "Can we afford Medicare for All?" *Boston Globe*, Jul 23, 2019. https://www.bostonglobe.com/opinion/2019/07/22/can-afford-medicare-for-all/QeLvk2h1McZQGBbqw6pQZl/story.html

Galvani, Alison, Alyssa S. Parpia, Eric M. Foster, Burton H. Singer and Meagan C. Fitzpatrick. "Improving the prognosis of health care in the USA." The Lancet, Feb 15, 2020. https://www.thelancet.com/journals/lancet/article/PIIS0140-6736(19)33019-3/fulltext

Garfield, Rachel, Kendal Orgera and Anthony Damico. "The Uninsured and the ACA: A Primer." Kaiser Family Foundation, Jan 25, 2019. https://www.kff.org/uninsured/report/the-uninsured-and-the-aca-a-primer-key-facts-about-health-insurance-and-the-uninsured-amidst-changes-to-the-affordable-care-act/

Gee, Emily and Topher Spiro. "Excess Administrative Costs Burden the U.S. Health Care System. Center for American Progress, April 8, 2019. https://

www.americanprogress.org/issues/healthcare/reports/2019/04/08/468302/
excess-administrative-costs-burden-u-s-health-care-system/

Goldstein, Robbie. "Don't let pharmaceutical companies ex-
ploit the COVID-19 pandemic." Commonwealth Magazine, Jul
17, 2020. https://commonwealthmagazine.org/health-care/
dont-let-pharmaceutical-companies-exploit-the-covid-19-pandemic/

Golshan, Tara. "Health care is getting more and more expensive, and
low-wage workers are bearing more of the cost." Vox, Sep 30, 2019.
https://www.vox.com/policy-and-politics/2019/9/30/20891305/
health-care-employer-sponsored-premiums-cost-voxcare

Gruber, Jonathan. "The future of health care? Affordability and inclusiveness."
Boston Globe, Dec 23, 2019. https://www.bostonglobe.com/2019/12/23/opinion/
future-health-care-affordability-inclusiveness/

Hill, Catey. "Despite Obamacare, a 'shockingly high' number of people know
someone who died after being unable to afford health care." Marketwatch.com,
Nov 13, 2019. https://www.marketwatch.com/story/despite-obamacare-a-shock-
ingly-high-number-of-people-know-someone-who-died-after-being-unable-to-
afford-health-care-2019-11-12

Himmelstein, David U., MD and Terry Campbell, MHA, Steffie Woolhandler, MD,
MPH.

"Healthcare Administrative Costs in the United States and Canada, 2017." Annals
of Internal Medicine, Jan 21, 2020. https://www.acpjournals.org/doi/10.7326/
M19-2818

Interfaith Center on Corporate Responsibility. "A Bitter Pill: The Human toll of unaffordable Medicines." Iccr.org, 2020. https://www.iccr.org/our-issues/health-domestic/bitter-pill-human-toll-unaffordable-medicines

International Federation of Health Plans. "2017 Comparative Price Report: International Variation in Medical and Drug Prices." Health Cost institute, Dec 2019. https://healthcostinstitute.org/images/pdfs/iFHP_Report_2017_191212.pdf

IRS. "The Health Insurance Marketplace." irs.gov, Feb 18, 2020. https://www.irs.gov/affordable-care-act/individuals-and-families/the-health-insurance-marketplace

IRS. "The Premium Tax Credit - The Basics." Irs.gov, Sep 19, 2020. https://www.irs.gov/affordable-care-act/individuals-and-families/the-premium-tax-credit-the-basics

Jha, Ashish K. "Ending surprise billing: A moral test for physicians." *Boston Globe*, Dec 9, 2019. https://www.bostonglobe.com/2019/12/09/opinion/ending-surprise-billing-moral-test-physicians/

Kaiser Family Foundation. "An Overview of Medicare." kff.org, Feb 13, 2019. https://www.kff.org/medicare/issue-brief/an-overview-of-medicare/

Kaiser Family Foundation. "Poll: Nearly 1 in 4 Americans Taking Prescription Drugs Say It's Difficult to Afford Their Medicines, including Larger Shares Among Those with Health Issues, with Low Incomes and Nearing Medicare Age." kff.org, Mar 1, 2019. https://www.kff.org/health-costs/press-release/poll-nearly-1-in-4-americans-taking-prescription-drugs-say-its-difficult-to-afford-medicines-including-larger-shares-with-low-incomes/

HEALTH ASSURANCE FOR ALL: INSIDE AMERICAN HEALTH CARE

Kaiser Family Foundation. "Medicare Advantage." kff.org, Jun 6, 2019. https://www.kff.org/medicare/fact-sheet/medicare-advantage/

Kaiser Family Foundation. "About 1 in 6 Emergency Visits and Hospital Stays Had At least One Out-of-Pocket Charge in 2017." Kff.org, Jun 20, 2019. https://www.kff.org/health-costs/press-release/about-1-in-6-emergency-visits-and-hospital-stays-had-at-least-one-out-of-network-charge-in-2017/

Kaiser Family Foundation. "Employer Responsibility Under the Affordable Care Act." KFF.org, Jul 2, 2019. https://www.kff.org/infographic/employer-responsibility-under-the-affordable-care-act/

Kaiser Family Foundation. "Health Insurance Marketplace Calculator." kff.org, Oct 31, 2019. https://www.kff.org/interactive/subsidy-calculator/

Kaiser Family Foundation. "A Dozen Facts About Medicare Advantage in 2020." kff.org, Apr 22, 2020. https://www.kff.org/medicare/issue-brief/a-dozen-facts-about-medicare-advantage-in-2020/

Kaiser Family Foundation. "2019 Employer Health Benefits Survey." Sep 25, 2019. https://www.kff.org/health-costs/report/2019-employer-health-benefits-survey/

Kaiser Family Foundation. "Total Number of Medicare Beneficiaries: 2018." kff.org, 2020. https://www.kff.org/medicare/state-indicator/total-medicare-beneficiaries/?currentTimeframe=0&sortModel=%7B%22colId%22:%22Location%22,%22sort%22:%22asc%22%7D

Kaiser Family Foundation. "Explaining Health Care Reform: Questions About Health Insurance Subsidies, Oct 30,

2020. https://www.kff.org/health-reform/issue-brief/
explaining-health-care-reform-questions-about-health-insurance-subsidies/

Kamal, Rabah and Cynthia Cox. "How do healthcare prices and use in the
U.S. compare to other countries." Peterson-KFF Health System Tracker,
May 8, 2018. https://www.healthsystemtracker.org/chart-collection/
how-do-healthcare-prices-and-use-in-the-u-s-compare-to-other-countries/

Kelly, Greg. "Medicare and Medicaid Participation Rates for Doctors
by State." Hcplive.com, Oct 20, 2016. https://www.hcplive.com/view/
medicare-and-medicaid-participation-rates-for-doctors-by-state#

Kennedy, Madeline. "Many U.S. cancer patients struggle to afford life-
saving medications." Reuters, Feb 22, 2017. https://jp.reuters.com/article/
us-health-cancer-drug-costs-idUSKBN1612NM

Khazan, Olga. "The Doctors Who Bill You While You're Unconscious." The
Atlantic, Feb 11, 2020. https://www.theatlantic.com/health/archive/2020/02/
surprise-bills-can-come-even-when-hospital-and-surgeon-network/606391/

Kiley, Jocelyn. "Most continue to say ensuring health care coverage is government's responsibility." Pew Research Center, Oct 3, 2018. https://www.pewre-
search.org/fact-tank/2018/10/03/most-continue-to-say-ensuring-health-care-
coverage-is-governments-responsibility/

Kinman, Tricia. "What Medicare Covers." Healthline.com, Mar 29, 2020. https://
www.healthline.com/health/what-medicare-covers

KomenAdvocacy.org. "Personal Stories about the U.S. health Care System." Jan 2009. https://ww5.komen.org/uploadedFiles/Content/GetInvolved/Legislation/Public_Policy/Personal_Health_Care_Stories.pdf

Kottasova, Ivana, Tami Luhby and Valentina Di. "She was asked to pay thousands for her coronavirus treatment, he got a free ride. She's American. He's Italian." CNN, May 1, 2020. https://www.cnn.com/world/live-news/coronavirus-pandemic-05-01-20-intl/h_3218141bd866a50189c82b04c221b9e2

Kroeger, Kent. "Why can European countries afford universal healthcare but not the U.S?" medium.com, Sep 26, 2018. https://kentkroeger.medium.com/why-can-european-countries-afford-universal-health-care-and-the-u-s-cant-966da2358e20

Lopes, Lunna, Audrey Kearney, Liz Hamel and Mollyann Brodie. "Date Note: Public Worries About and Experience With Surprise Medical Bills." kff.org, Feb 28, 2020. https://www.kff.org/health-costs/poll-finding/data-note-public-worries-about-and-experience-with-surprise-medical-bills/

Loth, Renee. "Response to COVID-19 reflects the nation's upside-down health care system." *Boston Globe*, Aug 14, 2020. https://www.bostonglobe.com/2020/08/14/opinion/response-covid-19-reflects-nations-upside-down-health-care-system/

McCluskey, Priyanka Dayal, Blue Cross's approach to paying doctors based on quality of care shows results, Harvard study finds." *Boston Globe*, Jul 18, 2019. https://www.bostonglobe.com/business/2019/07/18/blue-cross-approach-paying-doctors-based-quality-care-shows-results-harvard-study-finds/wf4GBM1Gi-ro2OevOyZCr0M/story.html

McCluskey, Priyanka Dayal. "What exactly is Medicare for all? It depends on whom you ask." *Boston Globe*, Sep 11, 2019. https://www.bostonglobe.com/

metro/2019/09/11/what-exactly-medicare-for-all-depends-whom-you-ask/u3JPg-2ZpY1JPHHJLzXKKlN/story.html

Merelli, Annalisa. "Depending on where they live, coronavirus can still cost Americans thousands of dollars." Quartz, May 20, 2020. https://qz.com/1853315/the-cost-of-coronavirus-care-depends-on-where-americans-live/

Miller, Emily. "U.S. Drug Prices vs The World." Drugwatch.com, Jul 27, 2020. https://www.drugwatch.com/featured/us-drug-prices-higher-vs-world/

Moore, Peter. "The High Cost of Cancer Treatment." AARP The Magazine, June 1, 2018. https://www.aarp.org/money/credit-loans-debt/info-2018/the-high-cost-of-cancer-treatment.html

Norton, Amy. "Cancer Takes Financial Toll, Even With Insurance." MedicineNet, Aug 10, 2017. https://www.medicinenet.com/script/main/art.asp?articlekey=205982

Osby, Liv. "People on Medicare struggle more with medical bills than seniors in other countries." Greenville news, Feb 13, 2018. https://www.greenvilleonline.com/story/news/2018/02/11/medicare-recipients-pay-more-medical-bills-than-seniors-other-countries/1063274001/

Panner, Morris. "Cancer Treatment Costs Imperil Patients." Forbes.com, Mar 25, 2019. https://www.forbes.com/sites/forbestechcouncil/2019/03/25/cancer-treatment-costs-imperil-patients/#64387142b6f2

Papanicolas, Irene, PhD and Liana R. Woskie, MSc, Ashish K. Jha, MD, MPH. "Health Care Spending in the United States and Other High-Income Countries." Journal of the American Medical Association (JAMA), March 13, 2018, Volume

319, Number 10. https://jamanetwork.com/journals/jama/article-abstract/267467
1?preview=true&site_id=654

Paradise, Julia. "Data Note: Three Findings about Access to care and Health
Outcomes in Medicaid." Kff.org, Mar 23, 2017. https://www.kff.org/medicaid/
issue-brief/data-note-three-findings-about-access-to-care-and-health-outcomes-
in-medicaid/

Pennie. "Pennie Plan Comparison Tool." Pennie.com, 2020. https://enroll.pennie.
com/hix/preeligibility#/results

Peter G. Peterson Foundation. "How Does the US Healthcare System Compare to
Other Countries?" pgpf.org, July 14, 2020. https://www.pgpf.org/blog/2020/07/
how-does-the-us-healthcare-system-compare-to-other-countries

PharmacyChecker.com, "70% of Popular Brand Name Drugs Sold in US
Pharmacies Are Imported; Cost up to 87% Less in Canada." News Release, Mar
16, 2020. https://www.pharmacychecker.com/news/70-percent-of-brand-name-
drugs-are-imported-cost-87-percent-less-in-canada/

Pollitz, Karen, Matthew Rae, Gary Claxton Cynthia Cox and Larry Levitt. "An
examination of surprise medical bills and proposals to protect consumers from
them." Peterson-KFF Health System Tracker, Feb 10, 2020. https://www.healthsys-
temtracker.org/brief/an-examination-of-surprise-medical-bills-and-proposals-to-
protect-consumers-from-them-3/

Rae, Matthew, Daniel McDermott, Larry Levitt and Gary Claxton.
"Long-Term Trends in Employer-Based Coverage." Peterson-KFF Health
System Tracker, Apr 3, 2020. https://www.healthsystemtracker.org/brief/
long-term-trends-in-employer-based-coverage/

Rae, Matthew, Rebecca Copeland and Cynthia Cox. "Tracking the rise in premium contributions and cost-sharing for families with large employer coverage." Peterson-KFF, Aug 14, 2019. https://www.healthsystemtracker.org/brief/tracking-the-rise-in-premium-contributions-and-cost-sharing-for-families-with-large-employer-coverage/

Rapaport, Lisa. "U.S. health spending twice other countries' with worse results." Reuters, Mar 23, 2018. https://www.reuters.com/article/us-health-spending/u-s-health-spending-twice-other-countries-with-worse-results-idUSKCN1GP2YN

Robertson, Lori. Fact check Medicaid' s doctor participation rates." USA Today. Mar 29, 2017. https://www.usatoday.com/story/news/politics/2017/03/29/fact-check-medicaids-doctor-participation-rates/99793460/

Rosenthal, Elizabeth. "Choosing a plan from the impossible health care maze." *Boston Globe*, Dec 2, 2019. https://www.bostonglobe.com/2019/12/02/opinion/choosing-plan-impossible-health-care-maze/

Rudowitz, Robin, Rachel Garfield and Elizabeth Hinton. "10 Things to Know about Medicaid: Setting the Facts Straight." kff.org, Mar 6, 2019. https://www.kff.org/medicaid/issue-brief/10-things-to-know-about-medicaid-setting-the-facts-straight/

Sainato, Michael. "The Americans dying because they can't afford medical care." The Guardian, Jan 7, 2020. https://www.theguardian.com/us-news/2020/jan/07/americans-healthcare-medical-costs

Sanger-Katz. "The Difference Between a 'Public Option' and 'Medicare for All'? Let's Define Our Terms." The New York Times, Feb 19, 2019. https://www.nytimes.com/2019/02/19/upshot/medicare-for-all-health-terms-sanders.html

Schoen, Cathy, Karen Davis and Amber Willink. "Medicare Beneficiaries High out-of-Pocket costs: Cost Burdens by Income and Health Status." The Commonwealth Fund, May 12, 2017. https://www.commonwealthfund.org/publications/issue-briefs/2017/may/medicare-beneficiaries-high-out-pocket-costs-cost-burdens-income

Schumaker, Erin. "Middle class Americans getting crushed by rising health insurance costs." Abcnewsgo.com, Nov 21, 2019. https://abcnews.go.com/Health/middle-class-americans-crushed-rising-health-insurance-costs/story?id=67131097

Scott, Dylan. "Coronavirus is exposing all of the weaknesses in the US health system." Vox, Mar 16, 2020. https://www.vox.com/policy-and-politics/2020/3/16/21173766/coronavirus-covid-19-us-cases-health-care-system

Serota, Scott. "Bolstering the Affordable Care Act is our best hope to insure all Americans." CNN, Aug 7, 2019. https://www.cnn.com/2019/08/07/perspectives/medicare-affordable-care-insurance/index.html

Singletary, Michelle. "Seniors report spending $22 billion from savings to cover health-care costs." The Washington post, Apr 22, 2019. https://www.washingtonpost.com/business/2019/04/22/seniors-report-spending-billion-savings-cover-health-care-costs/

Stevens, Lance and Lawrence Mallory. "U.S. Seniors Pay Billions, yet Many Cannot Afford Healthcare." Gallop.com, Apr 15, 2019. https://news.gallup.com/opinion/gallup/248741/seniors-pay-billions-yet-cannot-afford-healthcare.aspx

Szabo, Liz. "As Drug Costs Soar, People Delay or Skip Cancer Treatment." npr.org, Mar 15, 2017. https://www.npr.org/sections/health-shots/2017/03/15/520110742/as-drug-costs-soar-people-delay-or-skip-cancer-treatments

Terhune, Chad. "Life-Threatening Heart Attack Leaves Teacher With $108,951 Bill." Npr.org. Aug 27, 2018. https://www.npr.org/sections/health-shots/2018/08/27/640891882/life-threatening-heart-attack-leaves-teacher-with-108-951-bill

Tolbert, Jennifer, Kendal Orgera, Natalie Singer and Anthony Amico. "Key Facts about the Uninsured Population, Kaiser Family Foundation, Dec 13, 2019. https://www.kff.org/uninsured/issue-brief/key-facts-about-the-uninsured-population/view/footnotes/

Tozzi, John. "Why Some Americans Are Risking It and Skipping Health Insurance." Bloomberg.com, March 26, 2018. https://www.bloomberg.com/news/features/2018-03-26/why-some-americans-are-risking-it-and-skipping-health-insurance

Tozzi, John and Emma Ockerman. "What It's Like Living without health Insurance in America." Bloomberg.com, April 3. 2018. https://www.bloomberg.com/news/features/2018-04-03/what-it-s-like-living-without-health-insurance-in-america

University of North Carolina Health Care System. "Cancer patients miss appointments, prescriptions due to inability to afford care." ScienceDaily, Jun 3, 2016. https://www.sciencedaily.com/releases/2016/06/160603110806.htm

Vernon, Steve. "Don't make this dangerous Medicare mistake." CBS News, Apr 26, 2018. https://www.cbsnews.com/news/dont-make-this-dangerous-medicare-mistake/

Ways and Means Committee Staff. "A Painful Pill to Swallow: U.S. vs. International Prescription Drug Prices." U.S. House of Representatives, Sep 2019. https://www.cnn.com/world/live-news/coronavirus-pandemic-05-01-20-intl/h_3218141bd866a50189c82b04c221b9e2

Wikipedia. "health system." Oct 4,2020. https://en.wikipedia.org/wiki/Health_system

Witters, Dan. "Millions in U.S. Lost Someone Who Couldn't Afford Treatment." news.gallup.com, Nov 12, 2019. https://news.gallup.com/poll/268094/millions-lost-someone-couldn-afford-treatment.aspx

World Population Review. "Most Obese Countries 2020." worldpopulationreview.com, Apr 2, 2020. https://worldpopulationreview.com/country-rankings/most-obese-countries

Yeager, Kate. "Financial Toxicity and Patient Care." Oncology Nursing News, Jun 23, 2018. https://www.oncnursingnews.com/publications/oncology-nurse/2018/june-2018/financial-toxicity-and-patient-care

Zipperer, Ben and Josh Bivens. "3.5 million workers likely loss their employer-provided health insurance in the past two weeks." Economic Policy Institute, Apr 2, 2020. https://www.epi.org/blog/3-5-million-workers-likely-lost-their-employer-provided-health-insurance-in-the-past-two-weeks/

About the Author

This book fulfills Michael Metzler's long-time desire to explain in understandable and simple terms how the complex American health care system works and the need for change. Michael has had experience with health care access within the workplace, as a hospital executive, in the community, as a patient and as a caregiver.

His undergraduate and Ph.D. candidacy in Economics at Canisius College and Boston College, respectively, provided a unique perspective on the issues related to public health. His career began as Director of Labor Relations at a large food retailer and he served as trustee on several labor-management health plans. Over the next 25 years Mr. Metzler was first the Chief Operating Officer at a Boston teaching hospital and then CEO of a community hospital. Today as principal in his consulting practice he facilitates projects to establish collaborative models among community health care providers.

Michael is available for speaking engagements, podcasts and other opportunities for commentary and consulting. His contact information may be found at www.healthassuranceforall.com.

Made in the USA
Monee, IL
09 February 2021